CW00555880

THE AMATEUR ENTOMOLOGISTS' SOCIETY

BREEDING THE BRITISH BUTTERFLIES

by

PETER W. CRIBB

General Editor REG FRY

THE AMATEUR ENTOMOLOGIST

VOLUME 18

First Edition   1983
Second Edition 1990
Third Edition   2001

Copyright © 2001 The Amateur Entomologists Society

Published by the Amateur Entomologists Society
Registered Charity 267430
ORPINGTON, KENT, ENGLAND

Printed by Cravitz Printing Company Ltd.
1 Tower Hill, Brentwood, Essex CM14 4TA

Cover picture, White Admiral underside - photograph by Ian Rose

ISBN 0 900054 66 2

CONTENTS

FOREWORD

This handbook arose from a symposium on the subject held at the AES annual exhibition in 1981 at which the late Peter Cribb was joined by Harold Short, Richard Revels and John McFeely. There was so much interest engendered by those talks that Peter was asked to record the experience which had been built up by butterfly enthusiasts over many years.

In general butterflies are much more difficult than moths to rear continuously in captivity largely because of the difficulty in persuading the adults to pair in artificial conditions. The males of the vast majority of moths, even some of the day flyers, are attracted to the females by their scent and the females will generally accept the males without much persuasion. However most butterfly species rely on sight for their initial attraction and, although scent may also play a part in courtship, many species go through an elaborate aerial courtship ritual before the female is ready to respond to the advances of her suitor.

Despite these courtship requirements, captive breeding can be achieved using special techniques, including hand-pairing or even more complicated steps for the most difficult species. This edition retains all the techniques originally included, although the most drastic of these may be distasteful to many. We do not seek to recommend it, but to offer it as a last resort where captive breeding would otherwise be impossible and may be necessary for a species recovery programme. It is important that any new techniques should be recorded and published.

Apart from amending the 'useful references' and 'notes' on U.K. law laid down in the Wildlife and Countryside Act, which are to be found at the end of this handbook, we did not find any significant additional information on breeding techniques that justified amending the remaining text. We must, however, draw attention to one or two areas of information which have been overtaken by changes. One important change is that, due to the decline of their populations, it has now been made illegal to take any stage of either the High Brown Fritillary or the Marsh Fritillary from the wild. Also, on the topic of re-introducing butterfly species; considerable progress has now been made in re-establishing colonies of the Large Blue, Heath Fritillary and Chequered Skipper in southern England.

Finally, many people had reason to be grateful to Peter Cribb for his efforts on their behalf. He was frequently called on to help fight planning applications that would have resulted in undesirable changes to important habitats, particularly on common land. He also had a knack when it came to breeding butterflies and for nearly forty years he continuously bred the Marsh Fritillary in his garden. He was always willing to distribute live specimens from this and other stock to fellow entomologists and I personally bred this lovely fritillary from his stock for several years before passing on the progeny to other enthusiasts.

Reg Fry, January 2001

WHY BREED BUTTERFLIES?

Most of those who have an interest in insects have probably started by collecting caterpillars of the Peacock or Small Tortoiseshell butterfly as a child and had the pleasure of breeding them through and then releasing them back into the garden. Something had been learned and the entomological appetite may have been whetted. In past times the lepidopterist, in general, was concerned with putting together a representative collection of butterflies and moths and breeding species has been a means to that end — to obtain a series of perfect specimens, killed and set soon after emergence from the pupa. If one is in the process of building up a collection then this is the best method, not only ensuring the perfection of the specimens, but also being the least destructive method of collecting. A single gravid female taken in the wild can supply a series of insects for the cabinet and also frequently allows the collector to return live specimens to the original locality of the parent insect. His action has enhanced rather than diminished the wild population — something which pure collecting cannot do.

There are, however, more important reasons for breeding our butterflies and they entail not just the breeding out of a single generation but the ability to maintain a viable and healthy stock in captivity. Let us look at these reasons in some detail.

Breeding to study the life-history. Despite the work of such pioneers as the late F. W. Frohawk, there is still much to be learned of the life-histories of even some of our commoner butterflies and modern photographic equipment enables the amateur to record stages of growth and unusual phenomena to add to our total knowledge. Even where information is available in books, there is still great satisfaction in personal observation. One may also find that 'what has been written' is not the truth, or only part of it.

Breeding to study genetics. Today much has been learned in the wider field of genetics from the study of butterflies and this area of study is not closed to the amateur. Great fun can be had from breeding experiments, in the isolation of genetic features and testing out theories. Many of our butterflies have genetic features, sex-linked and otherwise, which can be investigated by the amateur as a means of learning genetic theory. One day a strange aberration may turn up and instead of putting it into the cabinet, it will be placed into the breeding cage and, with luck and some skill, further knowledge may be gained. Because of the relatively short life-cycle of butterflies, results can be obtained in just a few seasons.

Breeding for conservation. Today the great pressures on the environment have led conservationists to realise that in many instances the continuing existence of a species on this planet may rest on the ability of man to maintain stocks in captivity. From these it will be possible to return species to the wild in other suitable habitats. In the world of mammals we have good examples in the Pere David deer, the bison and the vicuna. Birds such as the Hawaiian goose have also been saved by breeding in captivity. The fast disappearing British countryside has meant that our susceptible butterfly species are also under threat and some have already been made extinct. The Large Copper, *Lycaena dispar* L. became extinct in Britain in the last century but the Dutch race, also living precariously, was introduced into Wood Walton Fen and since then has been maintained there, partially by breeding stock in captivity and boosting the wild stock by releasing. There are suggestions that the Large Blue, *Maculinea arion* L., should also be reintroduced from continental stock but in both these cases there would have been British stock available had there been those who were able to maintain stocks in captivity. Would it not be well today to consider those species most at risk in our countryside and the possibility of reserve stocks being bred by skilled amateurs to guard against catastrophe or the silent passing of another of our endemic species?

The return of stock from a single generation of a butterfly to the original habitat presents few ecological problems and is something to be encouraged, though one cannot recommend the return of large numbers from one female or of aberrant stock. The reason for the latter is that an aberration may be carrying a gene which can adversely affect a colony if introduced in an unnatural quantity. In my own breeding experiments I have found that the selection of an unusual genetic factor and breeding for this form has sometimes produced progeny which have within them lethal qualities which can decimate the stock. One would not wish to introduce this in quantity to a stable wild colony. However, the introduction of stock from one area into another or the return of in-bred stock to its parent colony is something to be avoided at all costs. It so often happens that a colony of one of our local butterflies has developed characteristics which enable it to survive in that particular habitat. Stocks of the same species but from other localities may have developed different survival characters which if introduced into another stock could cause the destruction of both. Continental races of our native species are suited to their own habitats and the re-introduction of the Black-veined White, *Aporia crataegi* L., for example, has proved to be unsuccessful. Only when a butterfly has disappeared completely from a known locality should there be any attempt made to introduce stock from elsewhere.

Another possibility is the introduction of a species into an area which appears to be ecologically suitable for its survival but where it has not previously been recorded. This is something which is worthwhile in the case of our butterflies — man is busy destroying habitat and the species that exist there and if conservation-minded entomologists can establish new colonies in suitable places to replace those lost by man's intervention, our fauna is not diminished. An example of this was the introduction some years ago of the Marbled White, *Melanargia galathea* L., to Ranmore Common in Surrey. If such a course is contemplated, the correct procedure is to survey the area as to its suitability, consult with fellow entomologists of the areas as to whether the species to be introduced is in fact absent, advise the County Trust for Nature that you have an introduction in mind and, finally, inform the Biological Records unit at Monks Wood, Huntingdonshire when the introduction has been carried out. The last is important as the Unit will then be aware of the possibility of records coming from an area which has not previously been notified.

The involvement of such bodies as County Trusts in any release schemes is a possible way of ensuring that the area of release is given some protection. Many successful re-establishments or introductions in the past have come to nothing because of the subsequent management of the release area. One well-established colony of the Marsh Fritillary, *Euphydryas aurinia* Rott., in Sussex was destroyed by the cutting and grazing of the common land and another of the Heath Fritillary, *Mellicta athalia* Rott., in the same county was swamped by the planting of conifers. Changes in management and neglect are two factors which adversely affect habitat and our butterflies are extremely susceptible to such changes. Current legislation gives no real protection, even to sites listed as being of special scientific interest, and perhaps the only long term hope for the species at risk is for the acquisition of suitable sites and their proper management, the latter aspect being one so often neglected.

PREPARATION OF FOODPLANTS

Before contemplating the breeding of any species of butterfly it is necessary to establish an adequate supply of the right foodplant and in this chapter I would like to consider some of the methods of going about this.

For breeding a single generation of a butterfly, it is possible to manage by using cut foodplant, provided a supply is available nearby and freshly-cut material is always available for the larvae to move on to. Cut soft-stemmed plants last fairly well in water, using clean rainwater in jars or bottles which have their tops plugged with cellulose wadding. Woody-stemmed plants are not so easy but can be made to last longer if the feshly-cut ends of the stems are placed into boiling water for about 30 secs. before placing them into the jar or bottle of cold water. An alternative to the jar or bottle is a block of 'Oasis', a material sold by florists for use in flower arrangements. It is soft and holes can be made easily into it for the plant stems. The block is then soaked in cold water which it absorbs and retains for several days. In hot weather evaporation can be reduced by wrapping the block round in polythene after it has been soaked and then piercing the holes for the plant-stems through the polythene.

However, for the majority of breeders many of the butterfly foodplants are not readily available and for the town-dweller probably none will be to hand. Such plants as horseshoe vetch, *Hippocrepis comosa*, and devil'sbit scabious, *Succisa pratensis*, and shrubs like alder buckthorn, *Frangula alnus*, have rather specialised habitats and the only way to have them available is to grow them. Thus the would-be breeder must first be something of a horticulturalist. How to set about it? There is now legislation which prohibits the digging up of wild plants and due consideration must be given to this so that many plants will have to be grown from cuttings or from seeds.

Seeds. It is possible to buy seed of some species but it is better to gather your own where possible. These should be gathered when ripe and sown in seed trays as soon as possible, using a John Innes seed compost. The seed should be just covered and firmed down, watered with a fine spray and then placed outside, preferably in slight shade and protected with a wire mesh from birds, mice, etc. Slugs and earwigs are a hazard to small seedlings and a liberal supply of slug pellets round the trays will control the former. Earwigs are not so easy and dead leaves and other rubbish which they use as hiding places should be cleared away. With plants which grow on chalk, additional chalk can be added to the compost and should certainly be added liberally to the potting compost for the next stage.

When seedlings are large enough to handle, water the tray well and then lift the seedlings, one at a time, and transfer them to small flower pots which have been filled with moist John Innes potting compost No. 1. Earthenware pots are best but not so easily obtainable today, plastic having taken over. The potted seedlings should be kept watered and as soon as established, the pots can be sunk into the soil in a suitable part of the garden for future use. All this will need to be done in the year before you need to use the plants. Larvae are quite voracious as they grow larger and you will need a lot of mature plants with plenty of leaves. The golden rule in breeding is never to have more livestock than there is feed available to ensure their coming to maturity. So be over-lavish in the number of plants you produce; none will be wasted.

Do not be daunted if you live in a flat or house with limited garden space. Plastic propagators can be used to raise seedlings and plants, provided you can get the proper amount of light to them. However, limited space will mean your livestock must also be limited.

Cuttings. A lot of plants can be most quickly propagated by means of cuttings. Plants as diverse as horseshoe vetch and sallow, *Salix* spp., can be grown in this way. Unless you have available to you such sophisticated apparatus as 'mist propagators', cuttings are best taken from ripe shoots of the plant, either pulled off with a heel or cut cleanly below a node. A compost with a high percentage of coarse sand should be prepared and potted and the cuttings, the bases first dipped in rooting hormone, placed into holes poked into the compost and firmed into position. The pots are then watered well and placed into a propagator. The moisture of the pots should be checked regularly. If a propagator is not available, an alternative is to use polythene bags tied over the pots. The purpose is to keep a humid atmosphere which will prevent the cuttings drying out before a new root system has formed.

Once the cuttings have rooted they can be removed carefully from the original rooting pot and potted up individually as with the seedlings.

ALTERNATIVE FOODPLANTS

Though many of our butterflies in the wild are ultra-selective in the plants on which they will lay their eggs, it is possible that larvae may be raised on alternative plants in captivity though the adults may be reluctant to lay their eggs on such plants. In the following chapters I will indicate alternatives that have proved to be successful and you can also consult the book 'Larval Foodplants' by P. B. M. Allen. Where females will only deposit successfully on a particular species of plant, the larvae will feed on a more easily obtained alternative, I have used a single plant of the former for laying and then moved the young larvae on to the alternative as soon as possible after hatching and this process has proved successful. A similar technique should be used in the case of rearing on artificial foods as described in the A.E.S. publication *A Lepidopterist's Handbook* (pp. 57-60).

Be prepared to experiment with untried alternatives but be sure that an acceptable foodplant is always available to return the larvae to if the alternative is not accepted. Some years ago, when breeding a large number of the Swallowtail, *Papilio machaon brittanicus* Seitz, David Marshall tried some on the Mexican Orange Blossom shrub, *Choisya ternata*, a most unlikely alternative, but the larvae thrived and appeared to prefer it to the common fennel which had been used for the remainder of the stock. Any successful alternatives not previously recorded should be published for the help of others.

FOODPLANTS FOR ADULT BUTTERFLIES

All butterflies need to feed as adults and proper provision must be made for this. They will feed on solutions of sugar or honey but often need encouragement to do so. This is effected by uncoiling the proboscis with a fine pin and bringing the end of it in contact with the solution. The solution in these cases is best handled by absorbing it into a cotton wool or cellulose pad until it is saturated. The butterfly is held by the folded wings between the forefinger and thumb and the tip of the proboscis brought to the pad. Once the butterfly has started to feed, the wings can be released and, provided the legs have a secure purchase on the pad, the butterfly will not move away until it is satisfied. Here must be given a warning. Strong solutions of sugar or honey should be avoided as it appears that there is a danger of re-crystallisation of the sugars within the abdomen of the insect. A sure sign of this is the distension and hardening of the abdomen and in females egg-laying stops and death follows. A suggested solution is 5% honey until a female starts to lay, when the concentration can be increased up to 10% which stimulates egg-production. It is better to underfeed the adults, provided a liberal supply of water is available at all times. Some species appear not to need flowers at all provided the foliage and ground of the cage is sprayed with clean water at regular intervals. Many species appear to prefer the mineral salts dissolved in the soil, in particular the Blues (Lycaenidae), and I have successfully used cattle droppings for this purpose for feeding the adults of the Chalkhill Blue, *Lysandra coridon* Poda. The Purple Emperor, *Apatura iris* L., is well-known for its preference for decaying material and often frequents middens adjacent to woodlands. Other species show a preference for honey-dew produced by aphids and this could also provide a source of adult food or it can be simulated by spraying honey water onto foliage in the cage. The danger in this practice is that it attracts ants and precautions must be taken to keep them out.

With flower-feeding species undoubtedly the best practice is to provide flowers which are known to be used by butterflies. Cut flowers can be used but quickly lose their ability to produce nectar and have to be replaced. The better method is to have suitable plants already growing in large pots or tubs which can be moved into the breeding quarters as they come into flower and so provide a natural source of nectar. Bee-keepers know that plants produce nectar most freely in warm humid conditions and these are fairly easy to simulate in the breeding cage. Plants such as *Buddleia davidii, Hebe salicifolia, Sedum* spp., asters, *Centranthus* (red valerian), grow quite happily in large pots and observation will give you others to add to the list. Thistles, particularly *Cirsium arvense*, are also easy to grow and the garden herbs such as chives, mint or marjoram are good plants and serve a double purpose. The advantage of such sources of food are that they can be safely left in the cages for the butterflies to use at will.

Another method which has been used with success is to use artificial flowers as an attractant to an artificial nectar source. Butterflies find nectar sources by sight and are attracted by the colour signal of the flower. This signal is not always the obvious one as experiments have shown that many flowers have areas around the nectar source which reflect ultra-violet light, not visible to us but clearly seen by visiting insects. Many insects have limited colour vision, seeing only part of the spectrum, usually the lower part (violet-yellow). The honey bee is blind to red, seeing it as black, but those reddish flowers visited by bees have been shown to reflect ultra-violet light. Artificial flowers, home-made or bought, can be very life-like and provided the colour is one that is recognised by the particular butterflies as a suitable nectar source, they will visit in search of nectar and if a small tube of sugar or honey water has been inserted into the centre of the 'flower', with a wick or plug accessible to the proboscis, it will be able to feed.

Colours which appear to be most suitable are the lower ones in the spectrum, violets, blues and yellows. Some of the silk flowers now available are extremely good imitations but simple flower shapes cut out of card have proved to be quite effective as the colour seems to be more important than the shape. One should experiment with colours and some of the startling paint colours now available could prove to be useful. Observation of butterflies in the wild should be recorded with notes on the colours of flowers visited, e.g. the Black Hairstreak, *Strymonidia pruni* L., seems to prefer white flowers, regularly visiting hog weed and wild privet blossoms.

Finally, the most important thing to remember with adult butterflies in cages is that they must have an available source of water. Cages bring about a micro-climate of which the temperature is always higher than that outside, particularly as black netting, the best for cages, absorbs radiant heat. This higher temperature can quickly cause dehydration and the butterflies will flag and soon die. In hot and dry weather it may be necessary to spray the inside of cages several times during the day. Water in troughs, etc. is not advisable as the insects will often fly or fall into them and drown. Lumps of 'Oasis' in shallow trays are a good idea as a water source and can be topped up with clean water each morning. I use a fine hand-spray and spray foliage, sides and base of the cage as necessary during the day but resort to the 'oasis' method if I know I am to be away from home for the day. One has only to watch butterflies when temperatures are high to see how dependent they are on moisture, often swarming on seeps and puddle edges. I have had them land on my bare arms to sip at perspiration there and have seen them drinking moisture from washing recently hung out to dry.

BREEDING CAGES

Cages for breeding butterflies are diverse and different sorts may be needed for different species or stages of breeding. There are two difficult phases in the life-histories of palaearctic butterflies, the first being common to all butterflies — the mating process; the second is overwintering. It is not possible to set down simple rules of management, as a system that works with one species may fail miserably with another. In this section I will describe the various types of cage without indicating their specific uses.

The Sleeve. This 'cage' is used in conjunction with a growing plant which is too large to pot up and insert into a normal breeding cage. The sleeve may envelop a branch, part of a branch or the whole plant. It is made of black nylon net for preference and resembles a large tube of the material, made by stitching the edges together. Both ends are open. The sleeve is slipped over the plant or portion of the plant and the bottom end is tied tightly around the stem using twine. This is important as a loose tie will enable insects and spiders to enter the sleeve up the stem, earwigs

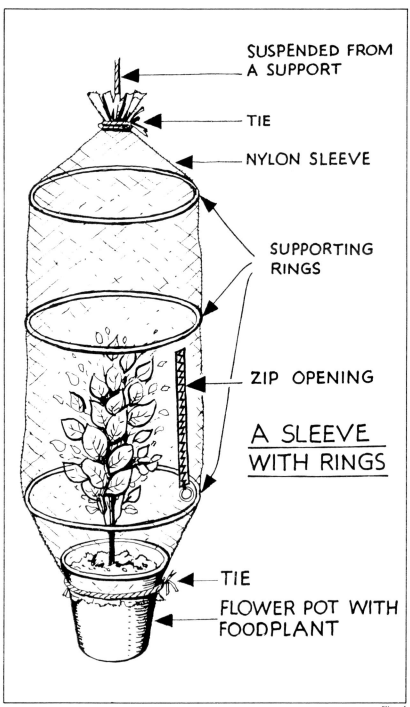

SUSPENDED FROM A SUPPORT

TIE

NYLON SLEEVE

SUPPORTING RINGS

ZIP OPENING

A SLEEVE WITH RINGS

TIE

FLOWER POT WITH FOODPLANT

Fig. 1

12

being a particular problem. The species to be bred (in whatever stage) is inserted into the sleeve at the open end which is then also secured with twine. In the case of a large sleeve, it is a good idea to incorporate a large 'zip' fastener at the side seam which will enable you to open and examine the contents without undoing the end-ties. Sleeves can be safely left for some time, provided spraying is done if adult butterflies are in the sleeve. Check at intervals that foliage is still available to larvae. This is a very natural way of breeding species and can be used for overwintering some species.

A form of sleeve can be made which includes supporting rings of copper or plastic-covered wire. Two or more rings are made to the circumference of the sleeve and slipped into it, the top one being positioned far enough inside to allow the top to be tied and then secured with stitching. The bottom one is inserted similarly and intermediate ones if thought necessary. The advantage is that the netting is kept taut and in wet weather does not sag and cause possible drowing of the inhabitants. It is almost essential if a sleeve is to house laying females as they are able to move about freely and exercise their wings (see Fig. 1).

Pot and Bowl cages. These are probably the simplest pieces of equipment in breeding. A flower pot or a plastic bowl in which the foodplant has been established is used. In the case of a plastic bowl, drainage holes should have been made in the base. Into the soil, in which the plant is growing, are inserted short canes, the tops of which are covered with plastic bottle-tops. Over the whole is placed a sheet of netting which is large enough to give an apron to at least half the depth of the pot or bowl. The insect is placed in under the cover and this is then secured by twine, copper wire, an elastic band or old nylon stocking placed tightly round the pot or bowl. The best elastic to use is 'knicker' elastic bought from a dressmaker as it lasts much longer and can be cut to the length desired. Rubber bands have a very short life and break with often unhappy results.

The pot or bowl is then stood in a water tray which ensures the foodplant has adequate water and also prevents the invasion of ants. This type of 'cage' can be used for laying females but there is a hazard. Females should be inserted when quiescent, usually early morning or late evening, or there is a danger of their escape while you are engaged in securing the net covering. The only attention needed is to see that there is enough foodplant for any larvae present and, in the case of adult butterflies, food and water are provided each day (Figs. 2 and 3).

Wooden cages. In the Society's publication 'A Lepidopterist's Handbook', instructions are given for making breeding cages from wood, cages which have doors and glass inserts. This type of cage has very limited uses in the breeding of butterflies and I would not go to the bother of making any for our present purposes. An effective cage can be made using wood as a frame only and then incorporating the 'sleeve' principle. A rectangular frame is made to whatever proportions are

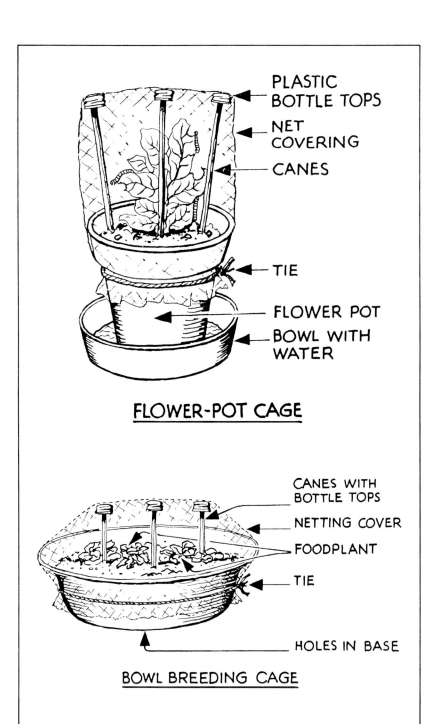

PLASTIC
BOTTLE TOPS

NET
COVERING

CANES

TIE

FLOWER POT

BOWL WITH
WATER

FLOWER-POT CAGE

CANES WITH
BOTTLE TOPS

NETTING COVER

FOODPLANT

TIE

HOLES IN BASE

BOWL BREEDING CAGE

Figs. 2 and 3

14

desired, using timber of a cross-section robust enough to ensure rigidity of the finished frame. Four frames made with halved joints is the simplest construction. These are then joined together to make the cage. For outside use the wood should then be treated with a preservative which will not be injurious to insects. For a large cage the corners can be fitted with extra braces to prevent distortion. A sleeve is made, large enough to fit round the cage and give adequate overlap at each end for tying. Again a zip-opener can be incorporated in one side to give ease of inserting the foodplant, insects, etc. The ends are tied securely. If it is desired to stand a pot, etc. in the cage, the base of the frame should be covered with a sheet of waterproof ply or aluminium. The cage can be stood on a suitable base or hung up. If stood, support should be provided against strong winds which would blow it over. If black netting is used, the contents of the cage can be seen easily and the problems of heat, condensation and unsuitable surface arising from the use of glass are avoided. Doors subjected to outside conditions never seem to fit properly and allow predators access and, for the amateur, doors are not easy to construct or fit. As an alternative to the wooden frame, I have used old metal aquarium frames from which the glass has been removed.

Collapsible cages. One type of collapsible cage is a sleeve supported by metal hoops. The large type of keep-net used by fishermen is very similar to this idea. Cages can be made as large as you wish, the size only being regulated by the strength of the hoops being used. For very large cages, the hoops are best made of plastic tubing. Lengths are cut to the circumference required (diameter $\times$ 3.1416) and joined to make a hoop by inserting a short dowel into the open end of one end and forcing it into the other open end. The dowel should be a tight fit. This type of cage is usually suspended and large ones will certainly be managed best by having a zip-opener in the side. On collecting trips they can be used in the field for getting females to lay and an alternative use can be made, with slight modification, as a butterfly trap using a suitable bait (this would apply in the main to collecting overseas for such species as *Charaxes*, *Apatura*, etc.).

Small collapsible cages can be made using dowelling and small blocks of wood drilled centrally through each face with holes to accept the dowels. This forms a frame which can then be slipped into a sleeve. Such cages are intended for use during field trips for laying females and are extremely useful, taking up very little room and being easy to assemble (Fig. 4).

Greenhouses. Some species of butterfly can be successfully bred in a greenhouse. The advantages are that the breeder has ample room to move and site his potted foodplants and nectar sources, the butterflies are able to fly about and act more naturally, and management is made easier as one does away with a lot of small units, several species being bred together in one place. It is possible to use a greenhouse frame without glass or plastic covering, covering the whole framework with netting.

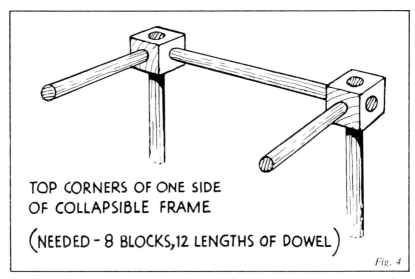

**TOP CORNERS OF ONE SIDE
OF COLLAPSIBLE FRAME
(NEEDED - 8 BLOCKS,12 LENGTHS OF DOWEL)**

Fig. 4

This avoids the greatest problems of the greenhouse — excessive temperatures and poor ventilation. Alternatively sections of glass can be removed and replaced by netted panels. If glass is used, then certainly outside shading will need to be provided if losses are not to occur. Temperatures inside a greenhouse jump dramatically in sunlight and can quickly reach a critical level, causing dehydration and heat exhaustion. If you are siting a greenhouse for breeding purposes, it would be well to have it in a position which comes into the shade when the sun is nearing its zenith and stays there until the evening. Many butterflies rest at this time of the day and the shading will fit into this pattern. If shading is done, it must be outside the glass as once radiant heat has passed through the glass it is trapped within the house. Glass is not a happy medium for butterflies to settle on and I overcome this by lining the inside of the house with netting which acts as a settling medium. Doors are a problem as flying adults will escape from them when opened for entry. To avoid this the simplest method is to hang a net curtain inside the door with a central divide, so that when the door is opened, any butterflies settled on the curtain can be driven off and entry is made by slipping through the central divide which drops into place behind you. Alternatively, in a large house a double door could be constructed, similar to that used in aviaries, the second door being in an alcove built inside or outside the house.

When constructing the house, care must be taken in sealing the floor to the frame so that ants, earwigs, etc. cannot enter by this joint. If the inside is totally netted it is not essential to seal other joints. Several butterfly farms have excellent examples of this type of breeding house and a visit to one would save many errors. One advantage of the breeding house is that it does allow the breeding of exotic species with the use of heat and light, but that is another subject.

Tubs. Some species of our butterflies thrive best if kept in as near natural surroundings as possible and one method of doing this is to use breeding tubs. Tubs can be made of almost any opaque material. Originally old potato tubs were used, being easily available, but these have now become scarce. I have found the ideal size for most purposes is a tub 18″ in diameter with a height of 15″ and I construct them out of opaque plastic, hardboard or sheet aluminium. Some I use are converted drums from old washing machines or have been cut from old plastic dustbins. If open ended, the base is buried in the soil for a few inches, foodplant is inserted, either planted directly into the soil or in sunken pots, and the top is covered with the usual netting and secured. The advantage of cylindrical tubs over rectangular shapes is that the covering netting can be held securely all round, making it insect proof. If tubs have bottoms, these must have ample drainage holes and can be placed on the ground and partly filled with a loam/sand mixture into which the foodplant is planted or sunk. For some species these tubs can be used for mating, laying, larval feeding, pupation and larval over-wintering. Do not use clear plastic for construction as this allows sunlight to pass through it, quickly raising the temperature to a dangerous level. Adults will also tend to bash themselves about trying to fly towards the light coming through the sides. The depth of the tub should be no more than allows reasonable movement of adults otherwise insufficient top light will be able to get into the tub (Fig. 5).

Other Aids. Because of the dangers of predation, it is sometimes necessary to collect up eggs as they are laid and place them into small plastic boxes. These boxes are available from many sources today and

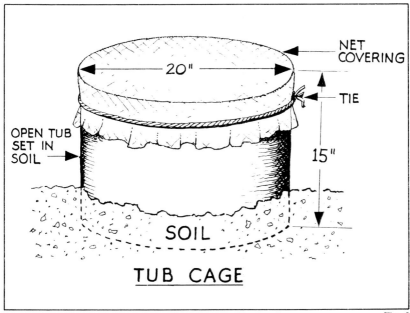

NET COVERING

20″

TIE

OPEN TUB SET IN SOIL

15″

SOIL

TUB CAGE

Fig. 5

most entomological dealers supply suitable sizes. The box should be lined with tissue paper to absorb any accumulation of moisture which might cause the eggs to go mouldy and the eggs, usually attached to small pieces of foodplant, are placed inside. The closed box is stored in cool shade and examined daily. As soon as the eggs hatch, the larvae should be given a small piece of fresh foodplant and when they have moved on to this they can be moved back onto the growing foodplant in the cage. Some breeders keep young larvae in boxes and feed them until they are large enough to handle easily but this does entail frequent examination and fresh foodplant daily. Frass and old foodplant must be removed regularly. While this may be practical for small numbers, it would become an unnecessary burden where large breeding stocks are involved.

I have found plastic two and four litre ice cream tubs to be useful for breeding purposes when in the field on trips lasting some time. They make suitable laying cages for many species. The appropriate foodplant, usually cut sprays with the bases inserted into a small water bottle or piece of 'Oasis' or cellulose wadding, is placed at the bottom of the tub, the female butterfly inserted and the top covered with black nylon netting secured by an elastic band. Kept in dappled sunlight with adequate moisture, this type of cage has proved successful for butterflies as diverse as the Swallowtail and the Small Mountain Ringlet, *Erebia epiphron* Knoch. The supply of foodplant should be liberal so that the butterfly keeps coming in contact with it as it crawls about on the netting. Many failures to obtain eggs from gravid females are due to making the laying cage too large so that the insect dashes about trying to escape and avoids contact with the foodplant. It is this contact which in many species stimulates laying. Some species, the Heath Fritillary for example, *Mellicta athalia* Rott., will even lay in a pillbox provided the foodplant is present and there is light and moisture.

Artificial Aids. As stated above, one of the problems in breeding our butterflies arises from the overwintering stage. Most species undergo diapause in one form or other — egg, larva, pupa or imago — the diapause being induced by length of daylight and temperature. By use of artificial daylight and temperature it is possible to defeat this resting period. Its main use is in breeding for laboratory purposes and this merits the cost. However, from the point of view of studying the life-cycle and conservation purposes, it has little use as the butterfly becomes completely disorientated as to season and survivors are adapted to an artificial environment. Some species cannot mature without the diapause and again this can be induced by artificial means using the ice-box or refrigerator to simulate winter conditions. Where specimens are only required for the cabinet, the life-cycle can be quite dramatically reduced in time by a combination of the aids referred to above but the breeding on of further generations may prove difficult.

However, these artificial aids can be used helpfully in breeding some of our difficult species, giving assistance to some awkward phase of the life-history. For example, females can be induced to lay freely indoors using artificial heat and light when one is faced with a spell of poor weather. Fluorescent light seems to be the most useful for this purpose. In over-wintering some species the constant dry temperature of the refrigerator can be a way of ensuring minimal losses. Many species have very heavy winter losses due to humidity which may cause larvae, eggs and adults to be invaded by moulds and uneven temperature ranges may cause larvae or adults to become active when they should be quiescent. A few species are susceptible to hard frosts, particularly among the *Erebia* spp., and the even low temperature of the refrigerator is ideal for maintaining quiescence without killing the larvae.

Predators. These are of major concern to the breeder and require fine-mesh netting and good ties as well as the use of sterile soil and clean foodplants. The main enemies are:—

1. Parasitic wasps and flies. Eggs, larvae and freshly-formed pupae are all at risk and must always be protected.

2. Earwigs. These will eat eggs, small larvae and soft pupae and are the most difficult pest to keep out. Their activities are nocturnal.

3. Spiders. These are the most insidious and are often present on foodplant in their minute stages and feed up on your larvae. Clean foodplants before use by dowsing them in water for half an hour which usually clears them of spiders. Check cages regularly for any that may have been missed.

4. Slugs. These will eat eggs, larvae and pupae. Sterilise all soil with boiling water to kill slugs and their eggs. This is most important in tubs set in soil outside.

5. Red mites. These are active for most of the early spring and summer and will attack eggs, larvae and pupae, sucking out the contents. I do not know how they get into cages but they do and should always be watched for. They move slowly but get there just the same.

DISEASE

I have found that there is less trouble with disease when breeding butterflies than there is with moths but this may be due to my having used more natural methods for the former. Diseases may arise from viruses, bacteria, fungus invasion or simply from adverse physical conditions or incorrect foodplant.

Larvae. Virus diseases can occur in the wild and I recall one occasion in the Spanish mountains where we came on hundreds of larvae of *Aglais urticae* and *Inachis io* feeding on a large clump of stinging nettles. The larvae were in the last instar and over fifty per cent of them were dying. Some virus infections result in the larva losing its appetite, then its co-

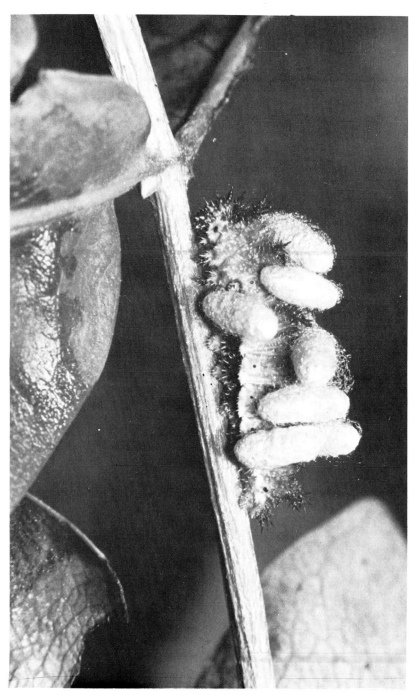

White Admiral larva covered with cocoons of parasite *Apanteles sibyllarum (photo: Richard Revels)*

ordination, the true legs not being able to grip and the larva hangs head down by its rear prolegs and anal claspers. Finally, the skin ruptures and the liquid contents pour out to contaminate the surrounding foliage and cage. Other forms also cause loss of appetite but the larva shortens and thickens, becoming hard. Eventually co-ordination is totally lost and it falls to the ground, hardening further and then shrivelling up. Bacterial infection is not so common but its results are rather similar to those described for the second type of virus. However, bacterial infection is also usually associated with a foul smell. Invasion of disease may be due to overcrowding, lack of cleanliness or its introduction with foodplant. Larvae are particularly at risk if bred in plastic boxes. Foodplant must be changed and/or checked daily, frass must also be removed and condensation controlled by the use of clean lining papers. Numbers should be limited to the space available so that larvae do not interfere excessively with each other. Even in breeding units outside similar criteria apply and overcrowding with its consequent increase in activity and metabolism appears to have an adverse effect on larval health and makes them susceptible to disease which may be latent in the stock. Foodplants gathered should be clean and dry and not gathered from places where spraying may be done or where dogs, etc. may have fouled them. One insect disease, *Bacillus thuringiensis*, is now sold as an insecticide spray. On one occasion I fed larvae of the Swallowtail on cut carrot-tops from a neighbour's garden and lost the lot with acute dysentery and then found out that the carrots had been sprayed against carrot-fly.

Do not be misled into believing your stock has disease by the appearance of larvae when they are about to undergo ecdysis. At the moult, larvae stop feeding, shorten and the head may appear to swell. Just prior to pupation, many species excrete a large amount of liquid with frass and this again may appear to be a case of disease. With experience you will appreciate the difference in these cases.

In the case of virus or bacterial disease, the larvae must be segregated and then destroyed and if contamination of the foodplant is suspected, this must be changed. B. O. C. Gardiner records that he has saved a stock by treating the foodplant with the antibiotic 'aureomycin', veterinary grade, and others have used T.C.P. Such measures should only be used if the stock is small and very precious. Infected cages can be sterilised using washing soda solution and then rinsed in clean water. Sunlight destroys infection and if possible drying should be done in the sun. Hands, forceps and any other equipment which may have come in contact with disease should also be cleaned thoroughly. Viral infections are highly contagious.

Fungal diseases are in the main a hazard of overwintering and are generally due to excessive humidity associated with poor ventilation. All breeding units provide a micro-climate which differs from that outside the unit and it is one in which moulds are able to flourish unless precautions are taken. Good drainage and ventilation and some protection from direct rainfall help to prevent fungal invasion of the larvae and with some species the provision of thick dry leaves which do not rot easily gives winter protection. The fungal hyphae can usually be seen, using a glass, extruding from the spiracles. The larvae go hard and mould eventually envelops them.

Wrong foodplant can be a cause of disease-like symptoms; for example, the race of the Large White (*cheiranthii*), which lives in the Canary Islands does not take to *Brassicae* (cabbages) but thrives on *Tropaeolum* spp. (garden nasturtium). Some larvae will not change happily from one foodplant species to another and develop intestinal trouble.

Ova. The main danger with eggs is fungal invasion. Left outside on the foodplant, this only seems to arise with species that overwinter as eggs and with these one should follow the suggestions given for overwintering larvae or resort to plastic boxes and the refrigerator. However, if eggs are gathered up on pieces of soft foodplant and placed into plastic boxes it is essential that the fragment of foodplant should be dried out thoroughly before placing it into a closed box. If this is not done, fungal hyphae grow from the moist plant fragment and invade the egg, killing the developing larva. This point should also be remembered when collecting eggs in the field, particularly in hot weather. I soon learned of this danger when collecting butterfly eggs abroad.

Eggs laid on woody stems, however, are in danger of drying out if kept indoors, even in plastic boxes, and the best method with these is to cut the supporting stems down to a node and immerse the ends in water until the eggs hatch. I prefer to tie the cuttings on a growing shrub or tree outside.

Pupae. Sometimes disease contracted by the larvae does not become apparent until after pupation. Any pupae which have discoloration are suspect and should be segregated. It is particularly noticeable in gregarious species. For example, in the Marsh Fritillary, pupae are normally white in ground-colour but diseased pupae may be bluish-black or reddish. In some cases the pupae look all right but fail to emerge and subsequent examination finds the contents collapsed and dried up. There is little one can do about it. Pupae which are kept over winter and which are gathered adhering to a section of the foodplant can be affected by fungus if the foodplant is not again properly dried before being placed into the sealed box.

HAND-PAIRING TECHNIQUES

Because of the difficulties of getting some species to pair naturally in captivity, many breeders use artificial means of mating them. Even for some species which pair naturally in captivity, hand-pairing is used as it ensures that mating does take place and that the right crossings in genetical work are achieved. I always pair my Swallowtails by hand. The reasons for the failure to pair naturally are diverse but their total amounts to an inability to reproduce the same conditions for courtship and pairing that arise in the wild. Flight patters, scent, touching and weather conditions all play a part. The age of the sexes is also often important. Male butterflies normally emerge a week or so ahead of the first females and during this period they feed and the gonads which will supply the viable sperms are able to develop fully. A newly-emerged male may be incapable of a fertile pairing. Females can be mated immediately their wings are dry but females that have been on the wing for some time may not be able to mate successfully and will start laying infertile eggs. As a rule for hand-pairing, one should select males which have been flying for at least a week and mate them with newly-emerged females.

The simplest technique is that described by Dr. C. A. Clarke in the Entomologist's Record and Journal of Variation, Vol. 64, No. LV (1952) and is a method most suitable for Swallowtails (*Papilio* spp.). The female and male wings are held together, either with the finger tips, one insect in each hand, or they can be secured with a paper clip. This prevents the insects fluttering. I hold the female in my left hand with the abdomen uppermost and the male in my right hand in the same position with the tips of the abdomens facing inwards (see Fig. 6). With the tip of my fingernail of my left hand I stroke and gently prise open the claspers of the male. As soon as they are open, I bring them into position over the area of the female's abdomen in which the ostium is hidden. In most cases the female will then extrude the ostium activated by the movements of the male's claspers. The male then grips the female's abdomen, engaging his uncus and when this is achieved the pair can be hung up in the breeding cage or sleeve. They should remain joined for some time, often an hour or more. Quick separation means that the process has to be repeated. If the female does not co-operate, slight pressure to the abdomen may make her extrude the ostium. This must be done very gently or she will be damaged. If pairing is not achieved at the first attempt, allow the butterflies to rest and try again, or try a different male if one is available. Be careful not to damage the legs of the female, as this may make it difficult for her to lay (Fig. 6).

For some species, e.g. the Purple Emperor, the stroking of the male claspers with the fingernail may have to be continued for quite a while before there is any response. It is not a task for those who bite their fingernails as the nail needs to project beyond the end of the finger far enough to slip between the two claspers.

In all cases one must be careful to position the male correctly. Incorrect positioning may mean the aedeagus entering the anus or even the ovipositor of the female and the resultant spermataphore blocks the passage and kills the female.

The males of many species have the claspers withdrawn into the terminal segments of the abdomen and the method described above is

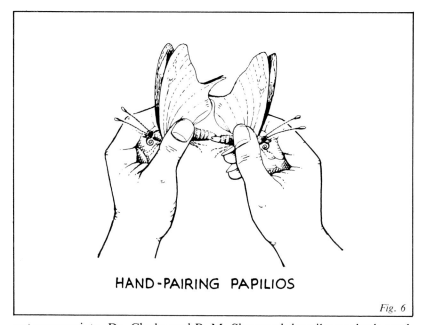

HAND-PAIRING PAPILIOS

Fig. 6

not appropriate. Dr. Clarke and P. M. Sheppard describe methods used by Lorkovic in the Lepidopterists' News, 1956 Vol. 10, Nos. 1-2 which are possible for these difficult species. It is drastic but Lorkovic had success with the Pieridae, species of Satyridae among the *Erebia, Pararge* and *Coenonympha* genera and some results with the genera *Limenitis, Neptis* and *Melitaea* among the Nymphalidae. He considered that the failure to mate was due to reticence on the part of the male, arising from adverse conditions, and by removing these psychological inhibitions pairing could be achieved. He therefore severed the head of the male or crushed it or crushed the thorax, so destroying the nerve centres which controlled the inhibitions. The method is to take the female with wings folded and place her on a flat surface, covering the wings with a slip of glass or a strip of paper pinned down. The abdomen is then brought forward and prevented from being withdrawn between the wings by means of a pin. The 'treated' male's genitalia are then brought into contact with the female's abdomen and the claspers opened using a fine pair of forceps. The two genital areas are then brought right together so that the uncus engages and the claspers lock in position. Thrusting movements should then occur by the male's aedeagus and as soon as this is observed the female is taken and hung up in the usual way. When pairing is complete, the male will fall away.

Another method described by a Japanese entomologist and by A. P. Platt (*J.Lep.Soc. 1969 p.109*) in regard to the hand-pairing of *Limenitis* spp. is similar but not so drastic. In this case the male is knocked out temporarily by inserting it into a cyanide killing-bottle. While still unconscious the same process as above is carried out. In many cases the shock of the cyanide causes the male to extrude the organs and open the claspers. The abdomens need to be held in situ until the male regains consciousness, when the claspers will be closed and a secure union made.

Such drastic means should only be turned to if it is shown that it is not possible to obtain natural matings or if the purpose of the breeding is to establish genetic experiments and positive known pairings are desired.

BREEDING METHODS AND TECHNIQUES

Having established the necessary foodplants for the larval and adult stages of the butterfly you intend to breed and constructed the cage or cages needed, you are now ready to proceed. It is possible to obtain breeding stock in any of the four stages. For many species the simplest way is to search for the eggs. Despite their being quite difficult to find, there are always many more of them than larvae, pupae or imagines, due to predation of the later stages. By experience one can recognise the type of plant normally chosen by the adult insect for laying and where to look for the eggs. It is also possible to watch females in the act of laying and collect up the eggs.

Collecting larvae for stock is the obvious method for such gregarious feeders as the Small Tortoiseshell and they should be taken as early as possible to avoid their being parasitised. Often batches of larvae collected in the later instars are found to be as much as ninety per cent stung either by ichneumonoid wasps or tachinid flies. The pupal stage is probably the least rewarding as they are usually carefully hidden away and most species that are gregarious as larvae will spread out widely to pupate. For species which are easy to net as adults, the simplest method of obtaining a clean stock is to take a female that has just paired. This means visiting the flying area about ten days after the males have started to emerge and either observing pairings or taking a female which is seen to reject the advances of males or is obviously bent on laying her eggs. Species which lay their eggs in a single batch can be examined — those with fat abdomens have yet to lay and will be suitable for your purposes. Several of our butterflies, those which hibernate as adults, do not pair until the spring so that they will probably be worn before they pair. With such species one should allow several days of good flying weather in the spring during which the butterflies have been seen to be active before taking a female for laying.

A factor of considerable importance in any breeding programme is the number of specimens that should be kept for breeding stock. The problem is that imagines do not emerge together or in any predictable pattern, other than the general observation that males are usually in advance of females. If only a few pupae are available, it often happens that the emerging butterflies arrive at intervals which do not allow proper pairing conditions and the stock may be lost. The other difficulty is that a small number of adults, possibly all from one parent female, will be too restricted in their genetic make-up to ensure a strong stock. Where it is possible, one should keep as many progeny as is practical and with a diverse parentage in order to ensure the retention of a viable breeding stock.

Two dozen pupae I would consider to be a minimum requirement. So often I have reduced my own stock by giving away to fellow enthusiasists, only to find that I have been reduced to the point where the stock is lost.

Many species when enclosed will lay their eggs on the netting of the cage or on the framework rather than on the foodplant. If it is desired to move these, they should be left for a few days to allow the shell to harden and then removed either by cutting up the netting or by using a soft-haired paintbrush moistened in warm water. The adhesive used to secure the egg is wetted and when softened the egg can be detached by using the tip of the brush. Some species, e.g. *P. machaon*, *A. paphia* and *F. adippe*, will lay on the inflorescences of the flowers of the nectar plants provided and I have had eggs laid liberally on the flowers of *Buddleia davidii*. Check all nectar plant flowers before disposing of them, using a hand-glass, or you may be losing your harvest.

Pupae should never be moved until several days after formation so that the exoskeleton can harden. For those secured to a silken pad, it is better to detach the pad from the support than to remove the cremaster from the pad, as the latter can sometimes cause part of the tail of the pupa to break off and remain on the pad — this inevitably causes death. For pupae with a cincture, this should be carefully snipped on each side at the point of attachment to the support as the silk is so strong that it will cut into the pupa if force is used to break it. To re-secure pupae, important for most pendant pupae, a drop of quick-drying glue such as 'Uhu' should be placed on the support (a twig or piece of netting) and before it dries the cremaster of the pupa is set into it. Unsecured pupae can give rise to crippled imagines.

Pupae should be sprayed with clean water from time to time if not kept in the open. If they are not, dehydration can quickly occur and this will result in death or in imagines which are not able to extend their wings due to the lack of water content in their bodies. Pupae should never be kept in containers exposed to direct sunlight unless there is complete ventilation as they can be quickly 'cooked'.

Using the Refrigerator for Overwintering. I use a plastic sandwich box with a secure fitting lid, the size about 8ins × 5ins × 2½ins deep and a series of small plastic boxes which fit in to cover the bottom, size about 2ins × 1ins × ¾ins deep. Into the large box place a layer of slightly moist peat about 1in. deep and on top of this place the small boxes with open tops. The larvae are placed in the boxes, two or three to a box, and the lid of the large box fixed. The whole is placed into the refrigerator which is kept around 38°-40°F. Species which hibernate in dead leaves should not be removed from the dead leaves before placing into the boxes. Overwintering eggs can be treated in the same way. Excess moisture must be avoided and if it appears that this is present on the inside of the lid of the box, this should be opened and the excess wiped off. The extremes are desiccation and moulds and half way between is the right condition. Larvae kept like this will remain viable up to six months and even longer. Pupae may also be retarded by using the refrigerator but with some species the imagines fail to expand the wings on emergence — this may be due to desiccation or to the retarding of the normal development of the pupa.

When bringing the larvae out of diapause, remove the box from the refrigerator and remove the lid, leaving the larvae open to room temperature and place a few shoots of the foodplant in each small box. These should then be checked daily and as soon as larvae are seen to be feeding they can be transferred to normal breeding quarters. Some species require sunlight to increase their metabolism so that they can start to feed and these will need to be placed on a windowsill or somewhere where they will have sunlight for a good part of the day.

In order that this booklet shall be as useful as possible to the would-be breeder, the following section will deal with each species or group or species in some detail, giving hints which have been gathered from the experiences of myself and colleagues.

The Swallowtail. *Papilio machaon* L. This species is now restricted to the Norfolk Broads in Britain where it is protected by law. It is however, important to know how to breed it in captivity as this may be one way of ensuring its survival as the habitat suitable for it is reduced. Its native foodplant is marsh hog's fennel, *Peucedanum palustre*, sometimes called milk parsley. It overwinters as a pupa secured to the stems of reeds and other plants in the reed beds surrounding the Broads and other waterways. It is on the wing in May, laying eggs on the fronds or flower-heads of the foodplant. The simplest way of collecting stock is as eggs or small larvae. The first instar larvae are black with a small white central girdle and are quite easily seen. The older larvae assume more protective colouring and are not so easy to find. They are usually full-fed by the end of June and pupate, some of the pupae producing a partial second brood of the butterfly in July. It is possible therefore to obtain livestock at almost any time of the year in one stage of another. In captivity the larvae will feed on garden fennel, *Foeniculum vulgare*, cultivated carrot, parsley and parsnip and on hemlock and *Angelica sylvestris*. They will probably feed on other umbelliferous plants as they do on the Continent. A garden shrub, *Choisya ternata*, has also proved an alternative. However, for egg-laying it is best to use the natural foodplant, fennel or hemlock (*Conium maculatum*). Pairing is best done by hand although they will pair naturally but it is rather 'hit and miss'. Once pairing has been accomplished, the female should be fed each day and kept in a laying cage in which the foodplant has been placed. The use of flowers for nectar stimulates laying. The cage must not be large or she will dash

Swallowtails mating *(photo: Richard Revels)*

about and try to escape. I have found a small cage, crowded with the foodplant, to be the best and on one occasion I had a female lay ninety eggs in a day in a plastic sandwich box covered with netting into which a dense spray of the foodplant had been inserted. The only treatment given was a liberal spray of tepid water. The eggs are beloved by earwigs and if there is any danger of their getting into the cage or sleeve, remove the eggs as they are laid and hatch them using the plastic box method, drying the plant pieces first.

In captivity you may find a good percentage of pupae hatch in midsummer and these can be bred on to further augment the stock. Select vigorous specimens of good size for breeding purposes and avoid deformed and aberrant ones. This goes for all species of course. If you want to breed for aberrations, you can do so but remember that you may have a degenerating stock unless crossings with normal strains are used from time to time, reselecting your aberrations in a later generation.

Larvae should not be crowded in a cage. In the wild they are solitary and in the last instar they eat voraciously. Also as they come to pupate, overcrowding may mean that other larvae which are still feeding can interfere with pupation. Overwintering pupae can be left outside but come through the winter well if placed in a large plastic box and kept in a cool shed, being brought out into a cage to emerge in April. The avoidance of 'drying out' of pupae is important as this results in deformed imagines. Do not put pupae into winter quarters until the end of September as there is an occasional late emergence during that month.

THE WHITES (*Pieridae*)

The Large White. *Pieris brassicae* L. This species overwinters as a pupa and produces two broods in the year. The first brood emerges fairly early in Spring, late April and early May; the second usually in July. However our native stock is vastly augmented most years by invasions from the Continent and the butterfly probably owes its continuing existence in Britain to the immigrations. This is because a very high percentage of larvae are stung by the wasp *Apanteles glomeratus* and as high as 95% of a batch of collected larvae will produce the typical silken yellow cocoons of the wasp instead of pupae. Stock is best obtained from caught females. It is a pest of garden cabbages and the eggs are laid in batches on the underside of the leaves and these can also be collected up. Alternative plants used in the garden are horseradish and garden nasturtium (*Tropaeolum* spp.). The butterflies normally pair quite happily in captivity and it is also possible to hand-pair them as the male claspers are quite large. The species is bred extensively in captivity for experimental purposes at the Department of Zoology, Cambridge where the larvae are usually fed on a synthetic agar-based food. The diapause of the second generation is brought about by the length of daylight and can be overcome in artificial conditions to produce continual

Orange Tip egg *(photo: Richard Revels)*

generations. In natural conditions the density of the black markings differs for the two generations.

The Small White. *Artogeia (Pieris) rapi* L. The life history and foodplants are generally the same as for *P. brassicae* but the larvae, which are green, feed singly after hatching from single eggs laid on the underside of the leaves. The larva works towards the centre of the plant and feeds secretively, being less affected by parasitic wasps and other predation. Stock is again best obtained from females which have been on the wing a few days after the Spring emergence. Larvae can be collected by searching into the hearts of young cabbages in the Spring or by watching females while laying and cutting off the leaves on which they have deposited.

The Green-veined White. *Artogeia (Pieris) napae* L. This is a butterfly of the hedgerow and woodland glade rather than the garden as it lays its eggs on the underside of the leaves of plants of the Cruciferae group growing there. It has a quite wide range of plants to select from and they will even use garden plants such as arabis, honesty and horseradish. Eggs are laid singly and the life history is similar to that of the Small White. While it is generally double-brooded, the Scottish upland race is single-brooded. This race and the Irish one is of particular interest to breed as are some of the forms which occur on the Continent. I have found horseradish the easiest foodplant in captivity as it grows readily from root cuttings and has large leaves.

The Orange-tip. *Anthocharis cardamines* L. The eggs are laid singly on the same plants as used by the Green-veined White but are placed on or close to the flowerheads, the larvae feeding first on the flowers and then on the seedpods. Members of the genus are single-brooded for this reason as their foodplants are only available in the Spring, the resultant pupae lying over from the late Spring until the following year. Sight of the males with their orange flash is a sure sign that Spring has come but the females are not so obvious and are easily mistaken for the other white species. By waiting by a clump of the foodplant, one can usually net a female in the act of egg-laying but I prefer to obtain stock by searching for the eggs. The flowerheads are turned up and the flowerstems searched. Newly laid eggs are greenish but quickly turn to orange and are then conspicuous. The whole stem should be picked and, when taken home, placed singly in a piece of wet 'Oasis'. This is necessary as the larvae are cannibals and do not like competition. There is seldom more than sufficient on one flowerhead for the support of more than one larvae and the 'dog eat dog' syndrome is one of self-preservation. Sometimes it is necessary to supplement the diet and the larvae will quite happily transfer to the green seedpods of honesty if nothing else is available. They will also eat the flowerheads of horseradish. Pupae should be wintered outside with protection from predation.

The Wood White. *Leptidea sinapis* L. This has a very restricted range today in Britain but has recently been reintroduced into woodlands in Oxfordshire with marked success. On the Continent it is almost ubiquitous and one wonders why our race is so retricted. It is a species which is partially double-brooded, overwintering as a pupa, so that it is on the wing in May and partially again in July. Eggs are laid singly on various leguminous plants, including *Lathyrus sylvestris*, *Vicia cracca* and *V. orobus* and bird'sfoot trefoil, *Lotus corniculatus*, being placed usually on the underside of a leaf. The butterfly lays quite happily in captivity but is a very fragile insect and will succumb quite easily if not given moisture and shade. If a specimen is boxed for taking home, the box should be large enough and a few moist leaves put in with it, particularly if the day is hot. For breeding, the easiest foodplant is bird'sfoot trefoil and a clump will feed quite a number of larvae to maturity. In the wild the butterfly visits bugle and other low-growing flowers for nectar and in the cage I have found chives are very useful for feeding the adults. Pupae should be watched, if the first generation, to see if some will emerge but once past July, they should be treated as for the Orange-tip.

The Black-veined White. *Aporia crataegi* L. This butterfly no longer occurs in the wild in Britain, having disappeared from its last haunts in the Isle of Thanet early this century. However, it is widespread in Europe, often occurring in thousands in some of its sub-montane localities and breeding stock can be obtained from such sources. Attempts to re-introduce it here in the wild have so far failed. The eggs are laid in a mass on the upperside of the leaves of blackthorns (*Prunus* spp.) and hawthorn (*Crataegus* spp.), being orange in colour and easily seen, rather similar to ladybird egg masses. The eggs should be sleeved outside on hawthorn or *Prunus* spp. The larvae hibernate when still very small in tight webs spun on the terminal shoots of the branches. Our damp winters do not favour the species and I have found quite considerable losses in the Spring due to moulds forming on the larvae and this may have been a factor in the demise of the butterfly here. Another danger is attack by parasites, *Apanteles* spp. again being the main culprit, and high losses occur from this, even on the Continent. Using plants grown in pots in a cold greenhouse seems to avoid the losses due to excessive damp and a stock has been kept going for some years using a greenhouse for all stages. Pairing does not appear to be difficult to obtain naturally. There is only the one generation each year and webs of larvae can be found both before and after hibernation but the larvae quickly leave the web in the Spring and cease to feed gregariously. The adult larvae look very like larvae of the Eggar moths (Lasiocampidae) and not at all like our other Pieridae larvae.

The Brimstone. *Gonepteryx rhamni* L. Stock is best obtained by netting a female in the Spring after the butterflies have been observed on the wing for some while. A fertilised female will be searching the hedgerows and rides for plants of alder or purging buckthorn (*Frangula alnus* and *Rhamnus cathartica*), its only two foodplants in Britain. The female can be sleeved in a large sleeve on a growing buckthorn bush and usually will spatter the leaves with its eggs. These are laid usually on the underside of the leaf, whitish when laid turning to yellowish-orange soon after. Eggs can be searched for in the wild and the females choose small solitary bushes in preference to the large ones or will use those sprays which project into rides in the woodland. Larvae can also be searched for by looking for eaten leaves and for the larva which lies on the surface of the leaf along the main rib. However, larvae are often parasitised by a wasp which produces a black white-banded puparium within the larval skin when the larva is about half-grown. Breeding on a second generation is difficult as the butterflies emerge in July, feed for a short period and then hibernate. Pairing takes place in the Spring in normal conditions but the butterfly is a very strong flier and a great wanderer so does not live happily in the confines of a cage.

The Clouded Yellow. *Colias crocea* Geoff. Although the butterfly usually reaches our shores every year, coming in over the south and south-west coasts, there have been years when it has come in thousands in late July and August. This used to happen with some regularity but the last 'Clouded Yellow' year was 1947 and since then the changes in agricultural usage on the Continent, where lucerne is now harvested several times in the year, have meant that no large build-up has been possible. The first migrations from the Mediterranean area occur in the Spring and some of these may reach us by May. These will breed to produce later generations, the butterfly being continually brooded, so that gravid females taken early in the year should provide a breeding stock for the year. Placed in a breeding tub with lucerne or red clover, the butterfly will lay its eggs liberally, creamy to start with and then turning orange-yellow if fertile. The larvae are easy to raise and the imagines will pair quite happily in a tub and lay further eggs. I have kept a stock going into November but the frost will kill the larvae or pupae and the only way to continue further is to resort to artificial methods, using heat and light. One of the interesting things that can be done with this species is to breed from the white female form, f. *helice* Hubn, as a means of studying a sex-linked recessive factor which is portrayed in the female. An explanation of the genetics is given in Amateur Entomologist's Society Bulletin (Vol. 35 No. 313). Stock can also be collected on holidays on the Continent where the butterfly is more often seen. I have done this successfully by using the four litre ice cream tub into which a clump of red clover has been placed (lucerne is very deep-rooted and difficult to lift). Cover the tub with black netting and spray with water, placing it in dappled sunlight. A mated female normally starts to lay almost immediately. As the eggs hatch very quickly after being laid, a daily examination should be made to ensure that emerging larvae have food available.

The Pale Clouded Yellow. *Colias hyale* L. This only reaches our shores as a rare migrant and many past records are suspect as until recently it was not appreciated that there were two species involved. Even on the Continent *hyale* is a much rarer insect than *C. australis*, having a more eastern distribution. If bred, it is easy to separate the two species, as *hyale* uses the same foodplants as *C. crocea* and should be bred similarly whereas *australis* uses only *Hippocrepis comosa* and its larvae have black markings. The larvae of *hyale* and *crocea* are very similar to each other. Unlike *C. crocea*, the larvae of *hyale* hibernate and can therefore be bred on without artificial aids.

The New or Berger's Pale Clouded Yellow. *Colias australis* Verity. The butterfly is common and widespread in western Europe including the Iberian peninsular wherever horseshoe vetch or *Coronilla* spp. grow. It is normally double-brooded and overwinters as a larva. The imagines are difficult to separate from *C. hyale* in the field but females flying low over slopes of the foodplant are almost certain to be *australis*. It is almost certain that many of the early records of *C. hyale* taken on the hills and downs in the south of England were of *australis* and in Richard South's book of British Butterflies the picture of the larva of *hyale* is that of *australis*, shown on its correct foodplant, *H. comosa*.

I have bred the species for the two generations from a female taken on the Simplon Pass which laid several dozen eggs in a plastic carton fitted with a clump of horseshoe vetch. The females are dimorphic, being either a white or a creamy-yellow in ground colour. I have not tried overwintering the larvae but a cool greenhouse should be effective. In Spain many of its breeding areas are covered with snow in the winter, so cold and dry conditions are probably the best for overwintering.

THE NYMPHALIDAE

The Small Tortoiseshell. *Aglais urticae* L. There are two generations each year in natural conditions, the imagines of the second brood overwintering, often coming indoors and hiding in dark corners. Pairing occurs after hibernation so that females for egg-laying should not be taken too early but after pairing flights have been observed. Eggs are laid usually in a single mass on the underside of the terminal leaves of perennial stinging nettle. When the larvae emerge they quickly spin a web around the terminal leaves and searching for these very characteristic webs is probably the simplest way of acquiring stock. They should be taken as early as possible as the species is subject to heavy attacks by parasites, both hymenopterous and dipterous, and I have had 90% losses of late collected larvae. In captivity one can use either annual or perennial stinging nettle and the larvae feed up very quickly, remaining loosely gregarious until the last instar when they feed singly, spinning the edges of a leaf together as a shelter. It is not advisable to crowd the larvae at this stage as pupating ones may be disturbed by those that are still active and may fall to the ground.

The first generation mates quite naturally in captivity and one can continue to the second which will emerge in late Summer. These should be fed and as the days shorten they will take up suitable hiding places in which to hibernate, though they will make short sorties in suitable weather until there are frosts. One method of hibernating them in captivity is to place sterile large pieces of bark into a cardboard box, insert the butterflies and cover with a strong fine netting. The box is placed in an outside shed in a dark corner. Cold seems to have no effect on our overwintering butterflies but high humidity does and the shed should be dry. I have kept them in a plastic box lined with corrugated paper in the bottom of the refrigerator and been successful. One needs a sympathetic wife or mother. When the species is observed on the wing in the Spring, the hibernating specimens should be brought out, fed and placed into a mating cage. These methods of overwintering adult butterflies can be used for the other species.

With many species of butterfly it has been found that the application of low temperatures (0°C) soon after pupation results in colour-pattern irregularities, mainly in the distribution of melanin, and some striking aberrations occur. The use of the refrigerator makes such experiments possible for the amateur and the Small Tortoiseshell is one of the species which lend themselves to this experimentation.

The Peacock. *Inachis io* L. The Peacock hibernates as an imago in the same way that the Small Tortoiseshell does and flies with it early in the Spring to pair. However, it is normally a single-brooded species and the eggs are laid later than those of *urticae* and webs of larvae will not be found until mid-May in most years. The eggs are laid in a mass on the terminal shoots of perennial stinging nettle, the females choosing clumps in full sunlight, often backed by a hedge or wall. The larvae are black and very spiny and fairly easy to separate from *urticae* after the first instar. Their feeding habits are similar to *urticae* and the larvae again separate in the last instar. The butterflies usually emerge at the end of July and after a fairly brief feeding period they find their Winter quarters, flying occasionally if the weather is suitable. Very occasionally there may be a second brood in August and I recall this happening in the very hot summer of 1976 in Middlesex but it is exceptional.

It is noticeable that bred specimens are often smaller than those occurring in the wild and this may arise either from insufficient foodplant being provided to ensure continuous development, from overcrowding which engenders greater activity or the creation of a generally higher temperature in the confines of a cage. In the case of the butterfly *Charaxes jasius* L., I have shown experimentally that larvae fed at higher temperatures produce imagines more quickly but of much smaller size. Underfeeding has been shown to have a similar effect.

The Comma. *Polygonia c-album* L. The Comma has increased its range in the south of England over the last fifty years and is now a common butterfly, even in the suburbs of London. It produces two broods each year, the life-cycle following closely that of the Small Tortoiseshell; however, the first brood has a large percentage of specimens which are lighter in ground colour on the upper- and underside, referable to the form *hutchinsoni*, and these produce the second generation, the dark forms normally hibernating early. The second generation are all dark and emerge in the late summer and autumn and feed briefly before hibernating. There is a fairly wide range of foodplants which include nettle, elm, hop, gooseberry and other members of the genus *Ribes*. The eggs are laid singly near the edge of a leaf and the larvae are solitary, being very distinctive with a white saddle mark and simulate a bird-dropping. Females taken after they have been on the wing for a while after hibernation will lay freely on nettle in a cage and I have also used a potted gooseberry bush for the purpose. Larvae can be searched for and normally hide under a leaf when not feeding — a beating tray can be used (if you don't mind damaging your bushes). Hibernation is spent settled on a tree trunk or similar site and I have found them on a wall amongst the ivy and *Ampelopsis*. I have never recorded it indoors like the two previous species.

The Red Admiral. *Vanessa atalanta* L. Each year in early summer there is a northward migration of the Red Admiral and in the south of England we normally see our first specimens in May. These will almost certainly be paired before they reach us so that females taken at this time will be suitable for egg-laying. The foodplant is again stinging nettle and eggs are laid singly on the young leaves, usually on the underside edge of the leaf. I have found the females like nettle which has just sprung up from nettle beds which have been cut. The larva will spin itself a small hammock by joining the edges of the leaf and it hides here when not feeding. These shelters can be found by searching and is one way of obtaining stock. The butterfly appears to be double-brooded here, the second generation imagines flying strongly in later summer and then migrating southwards, often appearing in large numbers to feed on fallen fruit in orchards before disappearing just as quickly on their journey south. There are records of specimens hibernating here and Alan Waters watched a specimen sunning itself on the Surrey Downs at the end of December. It might be worth trying to hibernate specimens bred in captivity and I would hazard that dry cool conditions would be necessary but frosts might prove injurious. This is an area for some investigation as I have no record of any attempts at overwintering the species.

Alternative foodplants to nettle are pellitory-of-the-wall (*Parietaria diffusa*) and hop (*Humulus lupulus*).

The Painted Lady. *Vanessa (Cynthia) cardui* L. The Painted Lady is an ubiquitous species, being found in every Continent except Antarctica, and is a prodigious migrant. Specimens come to Britain every year and sometimes in great numbers. The earliest record of arrival is in February when large numbers arrived in southern England, only to succumb to the next frost. Normally they arrive along with *V. atalanta* and will lay on most of the thistle family, including the cultivated globe artichoke. The creeping thistle, *Cirsium arvense*, is a favourite in England and readily available. The eggs are laid singly on the leaves and the caterpillar makes a hammock in a similar way to the Red Admiral. The species is continuously brooded and progeny bred in Britain in the late summer almost certainly make a southward migration towards the Mediterranean and North Africa from whence their progenitors came. Continuous breeding in captivity might be possible using artifical means for both pairing and maintaining a stock of foodplant. Migrating females which I have captured appear to have mated before reaching our shores as they laid eggs freely when confined closely on creeping thistle shoots. Young larvae should be transferred to growing plants so that it is not necessary to disturb them once they have made their leaf shelters.

The Large Tortoiseshell. *Nymphalis polychloros* L. The chances of obtaining a stock of British Large Tortoiseshells are today remote. The last strongholds were on the east coast in Essex and Suffolk where winters are drier and colder but a long series of mild and wet winters seem to have been too much for the butterfly. Casual sightings which occur most years are probably migrants and unless these are in the early Spring any females would be unmated. Today the best hope of breeding stock is from the south of France where larvae are common in early May, feeding on a wide range of trees. The larvae feed gregariously until the final instar when they separate and finally leave the tree to seek sites for pupation. The trees upon which I have found larval groups are cherry, wild pear, elm, hawthorn, sloe, sallow, willow and nettle tree (*Celtis australis*). There are probably others and they will eat stinging nettle. There is some parasitic attack but I have not found it to be heavy. The butterflies emerge in late June or July and feed up for hibernation. Tree sap and flowers are visited and they feed readily in captivity on a honey or sugar solution. For hibernation, a dry cool situation seems essential and I have successfully used a refrigerator. Humid conditions seem fatal and there are heavy losses from fungal invasion of the abdomen. Pairing in the Spring is best effected by releasing males and females, after feeding, into a greenhouse in which potted trees are present. Young sallows or cherry are suitable and the females normally lay their eggs in a closely-knit band round a small branch terminal, rather like the egg-mass of the Lackey moth.

The Camberwell Beauty. *Nymphalis antiopa* L. This is a casual migrant though in some years there are a large number of sightings. These are almost certainly specimens which have not paired. The adults go into hibernation early in the autumn unpaired and there is some evidence that some of these arrive in Britain in timber cargoes from Scandinavia. Unless a reasonable number of these arrived there is little hope of their pairing in the Spring. Again the best hope of stock is from the Continent, either as paired females or larvae. I have taken females in France in early May which I brought back in a refrigerator in my camper where they lay comatose. These were sleeved on a sallow tree after being fed and duly laid their egg-masses in the same way as *N. polychloros*. The imagines emerged in July and were fed over several weeks before they started to seek dark corners to hibernate. Those left outside all died during the winter, again due to apparent fungal attack, but those kept in a refrigerator came through the winter successfully. The larvae normally feed on sallow and willow trees but are also recorded on birch. In the south of Europe I have observed that the females first appear in the sub-montane areas and then move down into the valleys to lay. It is possible that the colder, drier conditions of the higher land are more favourable for hibernation.

The Purple Emperor. *Apatura iris* L. The breeding of this species in captivity was restricted to the capturing of a mated female for egg-laying or the collecting of ova or larvae in the wild and breeding them on to maturity. Mating in captivity was extremely difficult to achieve and the supplementing of wild colonies, as was done in Oxfordshire, was done by collecting wild eggs in late July and August and releasing the progeny in the following summer. However, Mr Harold Short has been able to hand-pair the species successfully so enabling him and colleagues to breed large numbers and obtain continuing generations.

In England the butterfly is now restricted to large woodlands of oak or beech in Hampshire, Oxfordshire, Sussex, Surrey and Wiltshire with possible outliers in Northants and Bucks. The loss of deciduous forest where the canopy covers the sallow trees has greatly reduced suitable habitat for the butterfly. To obtain stock the best method is searching for eggs in late July and early August. These are laid on the upper surface of the sallow leaf, the goat sallow (*Salix caprea*), being particularly chosen. The females prefer mature trees in shade and some are particularly favoured, probably being visited by more than one female. On one occasion I found twenty-three eggs on one tree. The first instar larvae are also fairly easy to find as they have black heads and sit at the leaf-tip. Once they have undergone the first moult they are difficult to see. In the Spring larvae can be found by observing where leaves have been eaten to the mid-rib and then searching around the spray. By the third week in May the larvae are usually nearly full-grown and easier to find. With the increasing scarcity of the butterfly, the capture of females for egg-laying is not to be encouraged unless it is certain that they have paired and the capture is in order to increase the stock of the area.

In hand-pairing Mr Short has found that the males should have been emerged 10-14 days before being presented to the female. Feeding should not be excessive and males should be allowed to fly for short periods and then kept cool and dark until ready for mating. After mating the females will lay in fairly confined conditions if well supplied with fresh sallow leaves, laying even in a shoebox under artificial light. A more natural method is to release fed females into a cage with a growing sallow bush. I mix up a mess of cow dung and wet it with slightly sweetened water, placing it into a tray on the floor of the cage, and the butterflies will come down to feed from this. Cages should be kept in shade as both the eggs and larvae are susceptible to excessive heat. Overwintering must be done outside with adequate protection against predators or, if in a greenhouse, spraying of the trees should be done from time to time to prevent larvae drying out. Hibernation takes place in crotches of branches, on the stems and sometimes inside dead leaves secured to the twig by silk. Occasionally larvae may hibernate on the ground in dead leaves so these should not be removed. The biggest enemies are earwigs which devour eggs and small larvae, and spiders which are a hazard at any time. Lacewing larvae will also suck the eggs dry. When the larvae are nearly full-grown they should be fed on the large mature leaves and this may mean cutting sprays for them if such foliage is not available on your potted trees. This ensures that the resulting butterflies are large and strong.

The White Admiral. *Limenitis (Ladoga) camilla* L. This is also a butterfly of the southern deciduous woodlands, the adults flying in late June and July along glades and in clearings. However, the females seek out the honeysuckle (*Lonicera periclymenum*) growing well under the canopy, preferring those plants growing up among coppiced hazel or round the boles of the oaks for their egg-laying. Captured females are difficult to induce to lay in captivity often dying shortly after capture. One method which has proved successful is to grow a honeysuckle up over a frame in a tub so that there are straggly pieces hanging down. The whole is then covered with a sleeve and the female inserted, keeping the whole well sprayed and in the shade. The eggs are laid singly on the upper surface of the leaf, usually near to the edge. These can be found in late July as well as the newly hatched larvae. The small larva eats away the tip of a leaf, leaving the mid-rib upon which it rests when not feeding. The leaf is quite distinctive and the larvae at this stage are easy to find. It is also possible to find the larvae in their overwintering hibernaculae, also when they leave these to sit on the leaf stems below the leaf in early Spring. At this stage they are still brown/white but in the final stages, when green, they are on the leaf lamina and not so easy to find.

For overwintering the larvae in their hibernaculae they must be kept outside and not disturbed. I keep them on a growing honeysuckle which is sleeved and placed under the shade of a hedge, not moving them into a cage until they have moulted once after hibernation. Wild-collected larvae will have a percentage with parasites which sting the larvae at a very early stage so that one must expect losses. Even eggs are sometimes stung and produce only minute wasps. I have never had success with natural pairing but it might be worth trying the Japanese method for *Limenitis*.

The Silver-washed Fritillary. *Argynnis paphia* L. The only practical way of obtaining livestock of this species is to net a female which has been seen to be paired or which is obviously busy laying her eggs. The eggs are laid normally in the cracks and crevices of tree bark, either on a standing tree or sometimes on felled logs or old stumps. The larvae hatch but remain hidden throughout the winter, having fed only on their egg-shell. In the Spring they descend to feed on dog violets growing on the forest floor, feeding singly and they are quite difficult to find. In captivity the females can be provided with pieces of sterile bark for laying but quite often they prefer to lay on the cage netting. I have successfully overwintered the larvae outside by sleeving the pieces of bark in a bowl planted with violets and left them in the lee of a hedge. In the Spring the larvae will find their own way to the foodplant and can be moved on when large enough to handle. Ordinary garden pansy is a good substitute for violet. The adults will pair naturally in a cage so that a continuous breeding programme is possible. In some areas the female dark form, f. *valesina*, occurs and this can be used as a useful demonstration of genetic inheritance, the dark colour being sex-linked. It is possible to avoid hibernation if only adult specimens are required. The newly-hatched larvae are placed into a refrigerator for about four to six weeks and then brought out and placed into artifical heat and light when they will start to feed and produce adults around Christmas. However, these will not be suitable for further breeding unless one is lucky enough to obtain a pairing.

The High Brown Fritillary. *Fabriciana adippe* D. & S. Today this is a rare butterfly in Britain, having disappeared from many of its old haunts over the last few years. It would seem that climatic factors have been responsible as many of the habitats have remained apparently unchanged. We have had a series of wet mild winters and this may have resulted in the loss of overwintering eggs. The larva develops inside the egg but does not eat its way out until the Spring. If one is fortunate enough to obtain a gravid female, it should be introduced into an open-based tub outside in which violets have been planted. A scattering of sterile dead oak leaves helps to simulate a woodland environment. The absence of predators is essential. Apart from feeding the female, nothing should be disturbed until the following Spring. As dampness is a probable hazard I place two battens across the tub, about 3ins. thick, to support a sheet of glass to cover the top of the tub. This prevents excessive moisture from rainfall but allows the passage of air. I use the same precautions for the Heath Fritillary, *Mellicta athalia* Rott., whose larvae overwinter in dead leaves, and the Small Pearl-bordered and Large Pearl-bordered Fritillaries, *C. selene* and *C. euphrosyne* which hibernate in dead leaves and rubbish on the woodland floor. Drying out, the other hazard, is avoided as water falling outside the tub will move through the soil to reach the plant roots and transpire into the tub. If it is desired to breed on in captivity, it is necessary to have stock from more than one female as I have found that there is a reluctance to mate amongst progeny of one female. This may be a natural phenomenon to prevent in-breeding and the use of more than one female does insure against this.

The Dark Green Fritillary. *Mesoacidalia aglaia* L. This fritillary inhabits a variety of terrain ranging from coastal dunes, chalk downlands to woodland glades. The larval foodplant is again violets, using the species of *Viola* present in the particular habitat. Mated females should be placed into a tub with dog-violets, *Viola canina*, and the violets shaded. Eggs are laid normally on the foodplant. As the larvae do not feed after hatching, other than on the eggshell, until the following Spring, it is a good idea to collect up the eggs on pieces of the plant as they are laid and transfer them into earthenware flower-pots which have been filled with sterilised loam into which a violet plant has been set. Sterile moss should be placed around the plant and the eggs placed on top. The whole is then securely covered with netting and sunk outside in a bank. The larvae will start to feed in the Spring and should be checked as soon as obvious eating of the leaves is observed. The larvae eat cultivated pansy and will also lay on this if wild violets are not available.

Note:— The larvae of A. paphia *and the eggs of both* M. aglaia *and* F. adippe *can be successfully overwintered in plastic boxes in a refrigerator, placing them there from September until the following March.*

The Small Pearl-bordered and Large Pearl-bordered Fritillaries. *Clossiana selene* L. and *C. euphrosyne* L. Both these species can be treated similarly and I use the tub method as for *F. adippe.* The eggs are laid on or near the violet plant and it is a good idea to pack loose moss round the plants as eggs will be laid on these and the material acts as an overwintering base. *C. selene* will produce a partial second brood in the south but winter is normally spent as a small larva. I have found these quite successfully by using a sheet in winter and shaking out the woodland debris over it. The larvae fall out of the rubbish and can be picked up and transferred to a breeding tub. I have collected the larvae of the Heath Fritillary in the same way. The main hazard with the two species is the loss of the larvae during hibernation from damp which causes fungal invasion.

The Marsh Fritillary. *Euphydryas (Eurodryas) aurinia* Rott. The reclamation of wetlands and the ploughing up of downland has meant that the Marsh Fritillary has now disappeared from many counties. It is an easy species to breed in large numbers in captivity and one which lends itself to re-introduction or establishment in suitable areas where its foodplant, devil'sbit scabious, *Succisa pratensis*, grows in some profusion. Collected larvae may be parasited quite heavily by an *Apanteles* wasp and the best way of procuring stock is to net one or two mated females or collect their egg-masses from the underside of the leaves of the scabious. The most successful way of maintaining a stock is to breed them in tubs sunk into the ground and into which scabious has been planted. As soon as webs are observed these can be transferred to alternative foodplants if scabious is in short supply. The three most suitable alternatives are cultivated honeysuckle, *Lonicera serotina*, Teasel, *Dipsacus fullonum*, or Snowberry, *Symphoricarpus* spp. There are about 300 larvae to an egg-mass and when bred in any quantity they consume vast quantities. Cut food in water is suitable but plug the containers well and check there is sufficient food every day until early August when the larvae will spin a communal purse-like web into which they crowd to spend the autumn and winter months. These must not be disturbed nor cossetted in any way. I keep the stock in tubs all the while and cover the tub only with a black nylon netting, giving no other protection from rain, frost, etc. Checks should be made for spiders and red mites which may have got in with foodplant changes. In the Spring the larvae come up to sun themselves quite early, usually in March in the south, and will start to feed as soon as the sun is warm enough to increase their metabolism. At this time of the year *Symphoricarpus* is not in leaf and I use teasel or honeysuckle if scabious is in short supply. Food is added as necessary and, as the larvae reach maturity, place a bunch of dried grass stems into the tub for the larvae to pupate in. Some will pupate on the sides of the tub and the netting as well. Do not try to move any pupae until they have hardened and keep the netting secure to avoid the entry of the wasp *Pteromalus* which attacks the newly-formed pupae. Mites will also suck them as well when soft. As soon as pupation is complete, prepare a new laying tub with *Succisa* plants and as the imagines emerge they are moved to this new tub and fed, and kept sprayed. Matings usually occur easily and last some while. A few days later the females commence to lay, choosing the plants in the sunlight and laying their mounds of eggs under the leaf tip. If the eggs are fertile they will change from yellow to a plum-colour after about a week and the round starts again. I have kept a stock of this species going for over 25 years and bred thousands of healthy specimens for release purposes in various counties in the south of England.

The Glanville Fritillary. *Melitaea cinxia* L. This species is widespread on the Continent where it is normally double-brooded in the south. The northern races are single-brooded and hibernate in August in purse-like webs, very similar to the Marsh Fritillary. In Britain it is now only found on the south coast of the Isle of Wight where it lives on the undercliff in colonies where ribwort plantain grows on dry sunny slopes. Paired females can be used to obtain stock or the easily-found webs can be lifted carefully in the Autumn. As one of the species under threat due to restriction of habitat, the Glanville should be taken sparingly for breeding only and stock returned to the same habitat the following year so that depletion does not occur from collecting. There are around 300 larvae to a web so that careful breeding should allow a good return with some stock retained for breeding on if one so wishes. I have kept stock for fifteen years in captivity without any noticeable deterioration in strength as long as one does not breed for aberrations.

Tubs are again the best method and Ribwort Plantain, *Plantago lanceolata*, the best foodplant. Winter webs should be left alone without protection from rain or frost. The tubs must be in a sunny well-drained spot. This is essential if the larvae are to start feeding successfully in the Spring. Breeders in the North may find it difficult to raise the metabolism enough to get the larvae to start feeding after hibernation and may have to use artificial light stimulus. In the South I kept a wild colony going in Middlesex on a dry railway yard for many years before fire destroyed them. Pupation tends to occur *en masse* in captivity and it may be necessary to break up the spun webs around the chrysalids so that the butterflies can emerge properly. In the wild pupation is done singly. Make sure that the wasp *Pteromalus* does not gain entry to the tub at pupation time or the stock will be destroyed. Pairing is done in the tubs and is very brief and not often observed. Eggs will be laid, whether fertile or not, but *do not* change colour if fertile so all eggs should be kept. They are laid in piles on the underside of a leaf. If you have Continental stock they may produce a second generation in late July.

Alternative foodplants are species of *Plantago*, *Veronica* spp. and possibly other members of the Scrophulariaceae tribe.

The Heath Fritillary. *Mellicta athalia* Rott. Although the Heath Fritillary is now a protected species and it is illegal to collect specimens, even for breeding purposes, it would seem sensible that those who have stocks in captivity should continue to breed them and pass surplus stock to others who wish to do so. The type habitat needed for the butterfly is not difficult to establish and provided the area is kept open it will keep to a fairly compact colony. In the past in Britain it has been a species which has followed the coppicer but on the Continent it flourishes in open woodland in permanent forest. The essential is sunlight which allows its foodplants to grow. The southern European race, *celadussa*, is more a hedgerow and wood margin species and I have found it commonly on roadsides near to woodland where the larvae feed on *Plantago lanceolata*. Breeding is best done in tubs as for the Marsh and Glanville Fritillaries but unlike them the larvae hibernate in ones and twos inside dead leaves, the edges of which are often spun together to form a hiding place. My own experience indicates that damp causes heavy losses in Winter and protection should be given from direct rain but with adequate ventilation. One method is to supply dead sterile oak leaves while the larvae are still feeding. When the larvae have moved into the leaves, place the leaves into an earthenware flowerpot which is sunk into the earth in a garden frame, the pot top being covered with a nylon stocking or netting. The frame top is left ajar so that rain does not fall directly on the pot but air can circulate. In the Spring the larvae start to move in April, coming up to sun themselves and they can then be moved back to the tubs onto growing *P. lanceolata*. In the wild the foodplant varies with locality — in Kent the main plant used is cow-wheat (*Melampyrum pratense*) whereas the old Sussex colonies used germander speedwell (*Veronica chamaedrys*), and those in the West of England are recorded from a wide range of plants including foxglove (*Digitalis purpurea*), *Plantago lanceolata* and yellow rattle (*Rhinanthus* sp.). In captivity it is also reported to have fed on antirrhinum. Pairing is not easily observed as it is brief and unmated females will still lay infertile eggs. These are laid in masses on the underside of a leaf, often right near the ground or on dead leaves. The larvae keep to a web until ready to hibernate, when they disperse and hibernate as described. Occasionally there may be a partial second generation and this does occur in the wild in the west of England.

THE SATYRIDAE

The Browns or Satyrs are all grass-feeders, and although in the wild they may have preferences amongst the grasses, in captivity they seem to take quite readily to grasses of the *Poa* and *Festuca* genera and will lay and feed on them. Young wheat shoots have also proved successful. All are best bred in tubs outside in which growing grasses have been established. Species which frequent dry grasslands need a well-drained tub and here the grass can be established over a layer of coarse sand. Care must be taken to exclude slugs when introducing grass clumps. Below are special notes on the different species.

The Meadow Brown. *Maniola jurtina* L. The larvae overwinter in a range of instars, much depending on the time of the season that the females laid the eggs. This accounts for the lengthy emergence period, from June to late August, but the species is single-brooded. Females lay freely on the grass blades and the larvae overwinter at the bases of the grasses.

The Hedge Brown. *Pyronia tithonus* L. As a woodlands species, use woodland grasses if possible and give some shade as larvae prefer dampish conditions. Single-brooded, overwintering as small larvae at the bases.

The Ringlet. *Aphantopus hyperantus* L. Also prefers woodland grasses and moist conditions. Single-brooded and overwinters as small larvae at the base of the grasses. The eggs are laid unattached to the grasses.

The Small Heath. *Coenonympha pamphilus* L. Usually double-brooded with a fairly lengthy emergence period so that one can see the butterfly on the wing from May to September in many years. The larvae from the second brood overwinter in grass tussocks. As its name suggests, it prefers drier conditions.

The Large Heath. *Coenonympha tullia* Müller. The natural habitat of the butterfly is in peat mosses where its main foodplant is beaked rush (*Rhynchospora alba*) but I have bred it successfully on *Festuca ovina*. Nice thick clumps of the grass give suitable places for overwintering and the larvae go deep into the tussocks to hibernate. In the south of England they tend to come up early to feed and should then be given some protection from frost. I move mine into the cool house but the imagines appear much earlier than in the wild so that the life-cycle of successive generations can get out of rhythm. North of the Midlands should provide a more natural environment for them and continual breeding should be easier.

The Speckled Wood. *Pararge aegeria* L. This is our only Brown to pass the Winter in either the larval or pupal form. The larvae may be in many stages of development and in mild weather in the Winter they may feed. The result is that there are a series of emergences in the Spring commencing with those that have overwintered as pupae, followed by those arising from the overwintering larvae. Each will produce a further generation and these will also be staggered so that in good years there will be butterflies on the wing into October in the south. In the breeding cage one could have almost a continuous emergence of butterflies from Spring to Autumn. The adults like dappled sunlight so that some shading should be provided and this can be done by placing cut or potted foliage to cast a shadow over at least part of the breeding tub. I have found it to be the easiest of the Satyrs to breed and the colour variations are of interest.

The Wall Brown. *Lasiommata megera* L. This is a species which is quite at home in the garden, even in the suburbs, wherever rough grass is left uncut in sunny places. For breeding, it requires well-drained sunny situations and almost any grass as a foodplant. There are two generations a year and the larvae hibernate, feeding occasionally if the weather is mild. There are different colour forms of the pupae and it would seem that the colour is induced by the background colour of the pupation site. Colours range from pale green to black. The eggs are laid on the grass stems.

The Grayling. *Hipparchia semele* L. Fescue grasses growing in sandy loam are the best for this species which needs a well-drained site. Eggs, in captivity, seem to be laid mainly on the netting of the cage so that it is a good idea to use an old piece to cover the laying tub which can be cut up later. Eggs should be kept in a plastic box until hatched and then the young larvae transferred to the breeding tub. Larvae will feed in mild weather in the Winter and hide in the grass roots when not feeding. The pupae form in the loose soil among the roots and the use of sand here is helpful. They should not be disturbed.

The Marbled White. *Melanargia galathea* L. As with the Ringlet, the eggs are not attached to the foodplant but are expelled from the ovipositor quite forcibly and fall into the herbage. They are hard white spheres and will bounce if they fall on a stone. Eggs are laid quite freely and I have had them laid in the pill-box on the way home. If predation is feared, they should be gathered up and treated in the same way as for the Grayling. Pupation is usually on the surface of the ground without any securement or covering and shortly before emergence the colour pattern is seen quite distinctly through the pupal skin.

The Scotch Argus. *Erebia aethiops* Esper. The distribution of this butterfly in Britain is restricted to the north-west of England and fairly widely in Scotland. On the Continent it has a much more varied range and occurs on dry downland and hillsides in conditions greatly different from those appertaining in Britain. It is apparent that our race has become adapted to the wet and colder conditions of north Britain where its main foodplant, blue moor grass, *Melinia caerulea*, grows. The eggs are laid attached to the grass stems and the small second instar larvae overwinter at the bases of the grasses, staying dormant until the Spring. They then feed up slowly to produce butterflies in August. In captivity they will feed on most grasses and overwintering is best achieved by using thick clumps of grass in tubs outside where rain and winter weather can get at them. The adults pair quite happily in captivity and one should be able to breed several generations once the right overwintering conditions have been achieved. In the north, conditions should naturally be easier to simulate than in the south where warm and mild winters may cause

Wall Brown butterfly egg laying *(photo: Richard Revels)*

problems. I would hazard that on the Continent the larvae do not hibernate completely and the butterfly is on the wing there in July.

The Mountain Ringlet. *Erebia epiphron* Knoch. In Britain the Mountain Ringlet occurs in the mountains of Cumbria and in some of the Scottish Mountains. In Cumbria it is normally found above the 2,000 ft contour while in Scotland it flies down to the 1,500 ft level, both being significantly above the lower level of Winter snow. This means that the hibernating larvae lie under snow during the Winter and are so protected from temperatures below 0°C. This may be an important factor in limiting the range of the species and precautions should be taken when breeding to prevent frosting of the larvae in hibernation. The eggs are laid freely on fescue grasses though the normal grass used in the mountains is matt grass, *Nardus stricta*. Hibernation takes place in the grass tussocks and I have placed these during the Winter into a frost-proof shed at night or when frost is present. This has proved to be successful in getting the larvae through the Winter. There are records of the larvae overwintering twice as do many arctic and high mountain species but I have not experienced this. The Scottish race is larger than that of Cumbria and with very variable spotting.

General observations. Richard Revels who has had a lot of experience in breeding the Satyridae and Lycaenidae for genetic purposes recommends that ova should be collected up after laying and hatched separately before returning to the foodplant. This is mainly due to the problems of predators, the chief being earwigs and slugs. It is worth the extra bother, particularly when one is dealing with small numbers or important genetic forms.

THE LYCAENIDAE
(Blues, Coppers and Hairstreaks)

Our native Blues are best raised using tubs in which their individual foodplant has been well established. Eggs and larvae are very vulnerable to earwigs and slugs and precautions are essential. Natural conditions should be maintained. Some species have symbiotic associations with ants, particularly ants of the genus *Myrmica*, and do not seem to suffer from their presence. I do not think that they are essential to their well-being, apart from the Large Blue of course. Larvae of the Chalkhill and Adonis blues which I have found in the wild usually have ants swarming over them, the attraction being the gland which secretes a sweet exudation. Although one can find both larvae and eggs in the wild by careful searching, the best method of obtaining stock is to secure mated females. Those with two generations a year should be taken in the Spring so that a second generation allows release back into the wild to the place of origin, keeping only sufficient for further breeding.

The Common Blue. *Polyommatus icarus* Rott. In the South this has two generations, usually in May and late July, the second being partial only as some larvae from the first generation will hibernate. The best foodplant is bird'sfoot trefoil, *Lotus corniculatus*, but *Ononis* spp. are also useful if available. The larvae overwinter well in the clumps of the foodplant. In the North the species is normally univoltine.

The Adonis Blue. *Lysandra bellargus* Rott. This species is now under great pressure because of the ploughing-up and over-grazing of downland. Its only foodplant in Britain is horseshoe vetch, *Hippocrepis comosa*, and this should be grown from seed or cuttings. It is deep-rooted and requires a chalky soil to thrive. There are two broods, each coming later than those of the Common Blue. The larvae overwinter at the base of the clumps of vetch when quite small. During their feeding period they hide by day under the plant sprays on the ground and feed as the sun goes down. Pupation is on the ground under the plant foliage. Eggs are laid on the stems and leaves of the vetch. Marjoram is a favourite nectar plant of all the Blues and it is worth growing some for this purpose.

The Chalkhill Blue. *Lysandra coridon* Poda. The problems of the Adonis Blue also apply to the Chalkhill Blue as both require the same habitat and foodplant. The latter has a wider range and occurs on most chalk downland in the south of England. It is, however, single-brooded, emerging at the latter part of July and on through August. Eggs are laid on or near the foodplant, often on grass, etc. growing around the vetch. In captivity it is a good idea to place sterile moss around the vetch so that the females will lay on this. The eggs will overwinter and for protection it is better to collect them up and keep them on a potted plant, securely netted, in a cold-frame outside and spray from time to time to prevent drying out. For pupation, moss around the base of the plant provides a good site as the pupae lie on the ground with a minimal silk web for protection. The many aberrant forms of this butterfly make it ideal for experimental breeding and Richard Revels and others have bred some of the more extreme forms in captivity for many years.

The Small Blue. *Cupido minimus* Fuessl. It is again necessary to grow the foodplant for this species in advance from seed. This is kidney vetch, *Anthyllus vulneraria*, and the butterfly lays its eggs on the flower heads. The larvae feed on the flowers and then the seed-heads, overwintering as a full-fed larva inside the dry calyces of the flowers and pupating in the following Spring there or on nearby grass stems. There is normally a single brood in Britain, emerging in June, but occasionally there is a partial second brood.

The Brown Argus. *Aricia agestis* Schiff. This is a double-brooded species and can best be bred in captivity on rock rose, *Helianthemum chamaesistus*. Storksbill (*Erodium cicutarium*) and other members of the genus and *Geranium pratense* are also used in the wild. Overwintering occurs as small larvae on the underside of leaves and pupation takes place on the ground with a few silken threads.

The Northern Brown Argus. *Aricia artaxerxes* F. This has only one generation, usually flying in July in the north of England and in Scotland where the rock rose is its foodplant. Otherwise its life-history follows that of *agestis* and Mr F. V. L. Jarvis has successfully crossed the two species. On the Continent the butterfly occurs as the sub-species *allous* Geyer.

The Silver-studded Blue. *Plebejus argus* L. The foodplants vary according to the habitat but for breeding in captivity it is best to use something which is not too tall for the tubs. Gorse, *Ulex europaeus*, is the plant most used on heathland localities but more convenient are *Ulex minor* and *U. gallii* which are dwarf or *Genista* spp. such as *G. anglica*, *G. tinctoria* or the cultivated *G. hispanica. Ononis* spp. are another alternative. The eggs are laid on the terminal shoots and do not hatch until the following Spring so are vulnerable during the period of hibernation to predation. The larvae have a close symbiotic relationship with ants, *Lasius niger* being one of the species, and a breeding tub might incorporate a nest of this ant for observation purposes.

There is only one generation a year, usually emerging in July. Pupation occurs low down on the basal stems of the foodplant.

The Holly Blue. *Celastrina argiolus* L. Hibernation occurs as a pupa and the spring butterflies normally choose the flower-heads of holly, *Ilex*, for egg laying but will also lay on the heads of *Cornus sanguinea* (dogwood) and bramble. The best method of obtaining eggs, apart from searching for them, is to sleeve a mated female onto a spray of one of these plants. Feeding can be done by placing a wad of cellulose soaked in sugar-water inside the sleeve, tied to a twig. Eggs should be gathered up by snipping off the sprays of flowers and each egg should then be secured to a separate spray in a second sleeve. The reason for this is that the larvae are cannibals and, if left all together, you may end up with one fat larva (which, in my experience, usually produces a female). A single spray of flowers is usually enough to support one larva. It bores into the flower bud and later eats the berries and soft terminal leaves. The second generation emerges in July and August and the resulting females will lay their eggs on the flower buds of ivy, *Hedera helix*. Pupae should be gathered up and kept in a plastic box for the Winter, placed in a cool shed. Pairing is best done in a ringed sleeve arranged over the sprays of the foodplant or in a large cage in which a potted flowering plant is placed. Both holly and ivy have to be mature to flower and holly is dioecius so that a female bush only will set berries and must be pollinated.

The Long-tailed Blue. *Lampides boeticus* L. The butterfly ranges widely in southern Europe and Africa and is an occasional migrant to Britain. It probably arrives in Britain much more frequently than is recorded as it is a fast erratic flier and quite difficult to see on the wing. In the wild it uses many members of the Leguminosae, laying its eggs on the calyces of the flowers. The everlasting pea, *Lathyrus latifolius*, is a favourite and I have found the clusters of flowers spattered with eggs. The late W. L. Coleridge gathered some blooms of this plant near Teignmouth in Devon and later found frass being extruded from the forming seed-pods. Searching discovered eight larvae which he bred out successfully. Perhaps searching flowers of this plant growing near the south coast might bring more to light. The species is continuously brooded so would need artificial heat and light to continue in Britain. The larvae will feed quite happily on french beans into which they bore. Other plants I have observed used in Europe are *Spartium junceum*, *Colutea arborescens*, runner bean and lupin. Larvae leave the foodplant to pupate and secure themselves with a girdle and remain as pupae for about ten days. At high temperatures the life-cycle is very short, about four weeks from egg to imago.

The Large Blue. *Maculinea arion* L. Although the Large Blue is now officially extinct in Britain, it is possible to obtain livestock on the Continent where it is still locally common. Lowland forms are similar to the British races but mountain forms are often heavily suffused with black scaling. The foodplants used for egg-laying are thyme and marjoram and females will lay on either of these if placed into a small cage. The larvae are said to have cannibalistic tendencies so should be kept separately. In the third (final) moult the larvae cease to feed and are ready for introduction into the nest of ants of the *Myrmica* species. Breeding on at this stage has been successfully achieved under artificial conditions by the establishment of ant colonies in a formicarium into which have been set inverted halves of walnut shells (or similar shapes cut from wood). These act as chambers into which the larvae can be introduced and fed on the ant larvae. Feeding ceases during the winter when ants stop breeding and continues in the Spring. The larva when full-fed takes up a position in the top of the shell-dome but falls to the ground to pupate. As the ants have been observed moving the larvae around with their own larvae, this may be part of the mechanism to bring the pupa up nearer to the surface as the ants move their own pupae towards the surface to gain heat from the sun. Although Frohawk refers to the butterfly crawling up from the depths of the ant-nest on emergence, I do not know of any proof of this and would guess that in the wild the pupae are moved towards the surface by the ants prior to emergence. The pupa is larger but of a similar colour to those of the ants. A description of the method of breeding is given by C. A. Clarke in The Entomologist's Record for 1954 (Vol. 66 pp. 209 et seq.).

For me there is some doubt about the host ants and the only time I found a female drying her wings, she was immediately above a nest of *Lasius niger* with no *Myrmica* nests in the immediate vicinity. *L. niger* is known to have many symbiotic associations and a lot more needs to be known about the butterfly and any successful breeding work would be a great help towards the reintroduction of the species to Britain.

THE HAIRSTREAKS

This is not an easy group to breed through with successive generations although I have had success with the Green Hairstreak. This can be bred using tubs but the others which are all tree feeders need to be raised in sleeves on a growing plant. The plants should be pot-grown and well established as the eggs will overwinter on the stems and the initial feeding will be on the plant buds.

The Green Hairstreak. *Callophrys rubi* L. The simplest foodplant for the species is the rock rose though the butterfly probably has the widest range of suitable foodplants of all our species, using different plants in differing habitats. Eggs are laid normally on the inflorescences and the larvae bore into the buds and later eat the foliage. Plants used are gorse, bramble, dogwood, *Genista* spp. and rock rose, in my own experience, and broom and other Leguminosae have also been recorded. The main problem in breeding is that the larvae are cannibals and large ones will devour smaller ones and newly-formed pupae. The safest method is to gather up the larvae as soon as they are large enough to handle and place them individually into plastic boxes into which fresh flower buds have been placed. The larvae will bore into the buds and should be checked regularly to see that they have sufficient food. I have used bramble buds when rock-rose buds are in short supply. Pupation takes place in leaf litter and a small plug of moss is suitable for this, the pupae lying over the winter. They can be kept in the boxes in a cool shed.

The Purple Hairstreak. *Quercusia quercus* L. As with all the hairstreaks that feed off trees it is necessary to have a small tree potted ready. Stock can be obtained by beating oaks in late May when the larvae are nearly full fed and are on the lower branches of the trees. Pupation in the wild is on the ground and moss makes a good medium for pupation. The adults should be fed by spraying dilute honey water onto foliage as the adults do not often visit flowers, preferring honey-dew. They can then be transferred to a pairing sleeve which has been placed over the potted tree. Feeding can now be done with pads soaked in honey water placed on top of the outside of the sleeve. Eggs are laid on and around the bud bases and will stay there until the Spring. Results are unpredictable and this goes for all the following species. If one is fortunate enough to net a mated female, it should be fed and treated in the same way.

The Brown Hairstreak. *Thecla betulae* L. The eggs are laid on the stems of sloe, *Prunus spinosa*, usually on or near a crotch. They overwinter and hatch later than any of the other tree hairstreaks. Finding the ova in winter is the easiest way of acquiring stock and these should be removed by cutting off a length of the stem. This is then secured to a twig of a sleeved sloe using twine and left there. Plum suckers and greengage can be used instead of sloe. Crowded larvae have a tendency to cannibalism, probably due to food shortages. Pupation in the wild takes place low down on the tree stems, the pupa being secured by a silken pad. In captivity they will pupate on leaves, the muslin or at the base of the stem. Feed the adults and after pairing is observed, place the females on sleeved sloe. They appear to need this for egg-laying.

The Black Hairstreak. *Strymonidia pruni* L. In the wild the eggs are laid on the upper stems of sloe, although in France I have found the larvae on bird cherry, *Prunus padus*. The eggs are not very obvious and stock is best obtained by searching for the larvae in the third week in May. Earlier the larvae are difficult to see. Later the pupae occur on the stems of the bush and are quite obvious though simulating bird droppings. Gravid females taken in the wild are unreliable for laying, sometimes spattering the foodplant with eggs and at other times laying only the odd egg. In view of the use of the upper branches of the bush, it might be better to sleeve a female onto a large bush if one is available. The butterfly does visit flowers and in the localities known to me it visits wild privet, *Ligustrum vulgaris*, and hogweed, *Heracleum sphondylium*. It is very important that newly-hatched larvae should be able to bore into the buds as soon as possible so that it is not wise to overwinter the ova other than on a growing plant. If eggs are found in the wild, cut the stem bearing the egg about nine inches long, to a lower node if possible, and place the stem in water. In the early Spring, end of March, secure the stem onto a spray of sloe which is growing outside so that the hatched larva can crawl onto a fresh bud. It seems that the young larva does not know what to do with young leaves and a plant brought inside may be too advanced for the larva to use.

The White-letter Hairstreak. *Strymonidia w-album* Knoch. The demise of the elm tree in southern England has made the future of this butterfly more than precarious and the chances of breeding it are now doubtful. Even in northern Europe the elms are affected and there has been widespread felling of elms to try to contain the disease, destroying some of the localities known to me. The butterfly in Britain has always favoured the wych elm, *Ulmus montana*, but will use other species. Suckers of these should be potted and allowed to establish before trying to breed the butterfly. Beaten larvae can be bred through on cut material but for successful egg-laying and overwintering it is desirable that a living plant should be used. Of course, if you have elm suckers in the garden, these would be ideal. The larvae first eat the buds, then the seed pods and then the leaves, pupating on the underside of a leaf or on a stem. The butterflies are very active and will feed on flowers such as bramble. In France I have seen them visiting *Buddleia davidii* and cut sprays of this would be useful for feeding the adults. The sprays wither quickly once cut and should be renewed daily.

THE COPPERS

The Small Copper. *Lycaena phlaeas* L. L. D. Young has bred this species successfully in captivity for many generations using clumps of sheeps sorrel, *Rumex acetosella*, grown in bowls. The larvae overwinter among the leaves of the clumps and are best treated naturally. Good drainage is essential as the butterfly's natural habitat is dry and sunny heath, meadow or downland. There may be as many as three generations in the year in the wild so that stock is not difficult to acquire at most times of the Summer, netting mated females. I have found the larvae but it is a laborious task and many are parasitised. The butterfly is subject to variation and aberration and is thus a good species for experimental breeding.

The Large Copper. *Lycaena dispar* Howarth. Although the original *dispar* is long extinct, two races of the species are still with us — *L. dispar rutila* Werneburg and *L. dispar batava* Obth., the latter still breeding at Wood Walton Fen in Huntingdonshire. I am indebted to Mr H. Short for the opportunity to breed *batava* and for his advice in so doing. I use a large cage which consists of a wooden frame, 6 ft. high by 4 ft. × 4 ft., with a solid wooden floor and a small door frame with door set into the side. The frame is covered with black nylon netting of a fine mesh. The cage is large enough to allow the butterflies to fly freely. It must be pest-proof against earwigs and clear of spiders and mites, which means the door must be well sealed when closed. A zip-closure is probably better. Plants of the giant water dock, *Rumex hydropalathum*, are potted up and placed in the cage together with growing or cut flowers of thistle, *Cirsium arvense*, or *Buddleia davidii* or purple loosestrife, *Lythrum salicaria* as a nectar source. Males and females are released into the cage and pairings should take place. It is brief and may not be observed. Eggs are laid on the upper and under surfaces of the dock leaves; they are small for the size of the butterfly. After about twelve days they hatch, the larva making a small hole in the centre of the egg-shell and then feeding on the underside of the leaf, making a channel in the tissue in which it rests. The channels can be seen from above the leaf as light passes through the leaf cuticle. In a normal year the larvae stop feeding by mid-August and prepare for hibernation. This is done by a slow change in colour from green to a reddish rusty colour which will match the colour of the dried dock leaves. This is where hibernation normally takes place, inside the curled dead leaves or sometimes among the dead inflorescences. Here the larva melds itself to the background on a silken pad. Experience has shown that the larvae overwinter best if kept in a cool dry place. Those left outside, to winter naturally, suffer a high loss due to the larvae going mouldy. Another method is to gather up the leaves on which the larvae are hibernating and place them in a plastic box in the refrigerator. In the Spring the leaves are placed back around the bases of the docks which are shooting up in the pots and soon the larvae will be seen climbing up the stems to start feeding again, changing back to their green colour. The larvae are voracious eaters and must be supplied with plenty of docks or cannibalism may occur. Pupation takes place usually on the dock stems but larvae may wander off the plant at this stage.

In a hot Summer, for example in 1976, a large number of the larvae feed up very quickly and produce a second generation, the imagines of which are a third or more smaller than those which emerged in July. This is a normal occurrence with *dispar rutila* in southern Europe.

The Duke of Burgundy. *Hemearis lucina.* Though not a lycaenid, this butterfly has many of the habits of that family. Its two foodplants are primrose and cowslip, *Primula vulgaris* and *P. veris.* The eggs are laid on the underside of the leaves in ones and twos and are quite easy to find. Alternatively females will lay quite happily in a tub. The small larvae eat holes in the leaves and if disturbed roll up and fall to the ground. I plant polyanthus plants in a tub and surround them with sterile moss. This gives a medium for pupation which is carried out at the base of the plants with no apparent fixture. The pupae hibernate and the butterfly is on the wing at the end of May and early June. Bugle is a good nectar plant and can be grown in the tub as well. If pupae are brought inside they often produce imagines in the late Summer and the butterfly is partially double-brooded in southern Europe.

THE SKIPPERS (HESPERIIDAE)

The Grizzled Skipper. *Pyrgus malvae* L. The usual foodplant is wild strawberry but the females will also lay on cultivated strawberry and *Rubus* spp. The best method of breeding is to use a tub in which clumps of strawberry have been established along with grasses to form a ground-carpet. Females can be introduced and apart from feeding them there is little else to do. Eggs are laid singly on the upperside of the leaves and the larvae feed on the leaf cuticle, hiding when not feeding in a small silken web. As it grows, the larva will form a shelter by spinning the edges of leaves together and pupation takes place in a cocoon-like mass of web at the base of the plants. Hibernation is in the pupal stage and the butterflies emerge in April and early May and will pair naturally in tubs.

The Dingy Skipper. *Erynnis tages* L. Treatment is as for the Grizzled Skipper but the foodplant is bird'sfoot trefoil, *Lotus corniculatus*, and the larvae which are full-fed by the end of August spin a hibernaculum using the plant leaves and rest there until the following Spring when pupation takes place without further feeding. In a good Summer there may be a partial second brood, something which happens regularly in southern Europe, and these specimens are usually more strikingly marked than those of the first brood.

The next species of Skippers are all grass-feeders and require grasses that grow to maturity and flower. For them the tub and netting covering must be tall enough to allow for this or a frame cage should be erected over an established clump of the grasses. The usual precautions against predators are essential as the cage or tub will be used for overwintering.

The Small Skipper. *Thymelicus flavus* Brünnich. Eggs are laid in the bases of the leaf sheaths of several species of broad-leaved grasses — *Holcus* spp., *Phleum* spp., *Brachypodium* spp. and *Agropyron repens* are all used. Females can be introduced into the breeding cage and fed on cut thistle flowers. Several eggs may be laid together in a sheath in a short chain and the small larvae quickly go into hibernation, spinning a small cocoon-like structure in the sheath. These should not be disturbed. In the Spring they start to feed and spin the edges of the grass blades together to form a tube-like shelter from which they emerge to feed in the evening. Pupation usually takes place in one of the shelters.

The Essex Skipper. *Thymelicus lineola* Ochs. In recent years this butterfly appears to be spreading its range in the south of England and is now recorded from many counties. It is a butterfly of rough grassland which is left undisturbed, flying with the Small Skipper but usually emerging slightly later. Breeding arrangements should be as for the latter but the Winter is spent as eggs which have been laid in short chains in the grass sheaths. The grasses used are again the broad-leaved species and couch and brome grasses seem to be favoured. The only sure way of identification is to net the females and examine the tips of the antennae which are black.

The Lulworth Skipper. *Thymelicus acteon* Rott. The life history follows closely that of the Small Skipper; the main grass being used in the wild is *Brachypodium pinnatum*. The egg chains are longer than with *flavus* and the larvae spin the small cocoon-like structures within the sheath soon after emerging from the eggs. They should not be disturbed until eating is observed in the Spring.

The Large Skipper. *Ochlodes venata* Brem and Grey. Eggs are laid singly on the underside of broad-leaved grasses, mainly *Brachypodium sylvaticum*. The larvae again spin the edges of leaves together to form shelters similar to those of the previous species and make a hibernaculum by spinning several blades together in which to overwinter. They feed up in the Spring and pupate in a similar structure.

The Silver-spotted Skipper. *Hesperia comma* L. Like the Essex Skipper, this species overwinters as an egg. In Britain the butterfly is confined to the remaining escarpments of our southern chalk downlands and many of its old habitats have been destroyed by the plough, scrub invasion or overgrazing. The eggs are laid singly on the leaves of sheep's fescue grass, *Festuca ovina*, and a good clump of this should be established in a tub with good drainage and a southerly aspect. Damp and predators are major dangers to the overwintering eggs. The larvae form in the eggs but do not emerge until April when they spin grass blades together as a shelter to feed from. Pupation takes place in such a shelter and the butterflies emerge at the end of July or in early August. Thistles are the best plant for feeding the adults. They are rapid fliers and will escape unless care is taken.

The Chequered Skipper. *Carterocephalus palaemon* Pall. This species is now on the protected list but is quite common locally in north-west Scotland where the main grass is *Brachypodium sylvaticum* growing in woodland rides and clearings. It will also use other broad-leaved grasses.

Essex Skipper eggs *(photo: Richard Revels)*

On the Continent it is common in woodlands and scrubland in both lowland and sub-montane areas. It is probably extinct in England but one can see no reason why stocks should not be bred for release into some of the old localities if these can be managed properly. Rides need to be open to the sun and the grasses allowed to flower. The eggs are laid singly on the grass blades and the larvae construct tube-like shelters in the same way that the other species do. Larvae are full-fed by late Summer and make a hibernaculum of silk and grass blades in which they rest until the Spring when pupation takes place without further feeding.

USEFUL REFERENCES

General

A Lepidopterist's Handbook by R. Dickson. 1992. 2nd Edition. Published by The Amateur Entomologists' Society.

Rearing

Breeding Butterflies and Moths - a practical Handbook for British and European Species by E. Friedrich (English edition ed. A.M. Emmet). 1988. Harley Books, Colchester.

A Silkmoth Rearer's Handbook by B.O.C. Gardiner. 1982. Published by The AES.

Identification

RSNC Guide to Butterflies of the British Isles by J.A. Thomas. 1986. Country Life Books, Middlesex.

Colour Identification Guide to Caterpillars of the British Isles by J. Porter. 1997 Penguin Books Ltd. London.

Foodplants

Larval Foodplants by P.B.M. Allen. 1949. Watkins and Doncaster. Kent

The Wild Flowers of Britain and Northern Europe by R. Fitter, A. Fitter, M. Blamey. 1996. HarperCollins, London.

Many useful articles have been published over the years in the entomological magazines on aspects of breeding British butterflies and the list below references those which are considered to be most relevant to this booklet. The species or the subject matter has been listed rather than the title of the article.

Bulletin of The Amateur Entomologists' Society

BRADFORD, E.S.	Vol.31, pp.134-136 (1972)	Breeding cages
BRUCE, R.	Vol.41, p. 22(1982)	*Thecla betulae*
CRIBB, P.W.	Vol.15, pp.39-40 (1956)	*Mellicta athalia*
	Vol.16, p.3 (1957)	*Mellicta athalia*
	Vol.15, pp.83-84 (1956)	*Colias crocea*
	Vol.32, pp.142-144(1973)	*Colias crocea*
	Vol.23, pp.116-118 (1964)	*Apatura iris*
	Vol.24, pp.13-14 (1965)	*Apatura iris*
	Vol.28, pp.41-44 (1969)	*Apatura iris*
	Vol.38, pp.89-90 (1979)	*Apatura iris*
	Vol.26, pp.50-51(1967)	*Colias australis*
	Vol.29, pp.38-40 (1970)	*Thecla betulae*
	Vol.40, pp.19-20 (1981)	*Limenitis camilla* Egg-laying habits
	Vol.47, pp.176-177 (1988)	*Euphydryas aurinia*
DENNIS, R.	Vol.44, pp.77-81(1985)	*Pieris napi* Egg-laying sites
DRAKE, J.RH	Vol.18, pp.78-79 (1959)	*Papilio machaon*
FRY, R.A.	Vol 57 pp.25-28 (1998)	Overwintering (moth) larvae
GARDINER, B.O.C.	Vol.32, pp.159-163 (1973)	Obtaining eggs in captivity
GREY, P.R.	Vol.31, pp.58-59 (1972)	*Quercusia quercus*
HOBBS, T.A.	Vol.46, pp.164-177 (1987)	*Quercusia quercus*
ILSE, D.	Vol.15, pp.75 (1956)	Feeding response to colour in *Papilio demoleus*
JARMAN, R.A.	Vol.19, pp.51-52 (1960)	*Colias crocea*
KEMP, R.	Vol.57, p. 48 (1998)	*Aricia agestis*

McNAMARA, D.	Vol.44, pp.179-181(1985)	*Anthocharis cardamines*
	Vol.46, pp.143-145 (1987)	*Euphydryas aurinia*
MARTIN, P.A.	Vol.38, pp.42-43 (1979)	Cages for cannibal larvae
PLATTS, J.	Vol.32, pp.133-134 (1973)	*Argynnis paphia*
PLESTER, L.	Vol.34, pp.30-34 (1975)	*Nymphalis antiopa*
	Vol.34, pp.73-76 (1975)	Juice pods for butterflies
PORTER, K.	Vol.34, pp.19-20 (1975)	*Erebia epiphron*
	Vol.35, pp.33-39	Genetics for breeding
	pp.163-167 (1976)	lepidoptera
ROBERTSON, T.S.	Vol.22, pp.16-17 (1963)	*Limenitis camilla*
	Vol.28, pp.114-115 (1969)	*Lysandra bellargus*
	Vol.29, pp.40-42 (1970)	*Anthocharis cardamines*
	Vol.30, pp.128-129(1971)	*Celastrina argiolus*
SHAW, G.	Vol.30, pp.125-128 (1971)	*Polyommatus icarus*
SMITH, J.A.D.	Vol.43, pp.169-171(1984)	*Lysandra bellargus* Effect
		of grazing on populations
STALLWOOD, B.R.	Vol.31, pp.25-28 (1972)	Feeding habits of adult
	pp.54-56,130-132	butterflies
	Vol.32, pp.64-72 (1973)	Feeding habits of adult
	pp.108-114,174-181	butterflies
	Vol.38, pp.194-196(1979)	-ditto-
	Vol.40, pp.161-164(1981)	*Melanargia galathea*
ULRICH K.J.	Vol 45, pp.210 (1986)	*Argynnis paphia*

The Entomologist's Record

BARRINGTON,.R.	Vol.106, pp.13-15 (1994)	*Maniola jurtina*
CHALMERS-HUNT, J	Vol.88, pp.89-104 (1976)	*Nymphalis antiopa*
GARDINER, B.O.C.	Vol.90, pp.181-184,	Preparing artificial diets
	pp.287-291(1978)	for Lepidoptera
	Vol.99, pp.161-168 (1987)	*Cynthia cardui*
GREEN, J.E.	Vol.102, pp.253-266 (1990)	*Thecla betulae*
HYDE, G.E.	Vol.84, p.24 (1972)	*Clossiana selene*
LEMPKE, B.J.	Vol.83, pp.199-203 (1971)	*Vanessa atalanta*
LIPSCOMBE, C.G.	Vol.80, pp.284-285 (1968)	*Lysandra coridon*
	Vol.83, pp.333-335 (1971)	*Maniola jurtina*
LUCKENS, C.J.	Vol.90, pp.108-112(1978)	*Euphydryas aurinia*
McFEELY, J.	Vol.91, pp.141-142 (1979)	*Strymonidia w-album*
PAYNE, J.	Vol.93, pp.11-12 (1981)	*Leptidea sinapis*
PULLIN, A.S.	Vol 98, pp.9-10 (1986)	*Aglias urticae*
REVELS, RH	Vol.87, pp.281-283 (1975)	*Lysandra coridon*
	Vol.87, pp.283-285 (1975)	*Aphantopus hyperantus*
	Vol.89, pp.45-46 (1977)	*Lysandra coridon*
	Vol.89, pp.43-44 (1977)	*Pyronia tithonus*
	Vol.90, pp.159-161(1978)	*Hipparchia semele*
	Vol.92, pp.57-60 (1980)	*Melanargia semele*
SHORT, H.G.	Vol.79, pp.306-307 (1967)	*Nymphalis polychlorus*
	Vol.89, pp.62-63 (1977)	*Apatura iris*
THOMSON, G.	Vol.85, pp.109-114(1973)	*Maniola jurtina*
TILLEY, R.J.	Vol.96, pp.141-143 (1984)	*Lycaena dispar*
TOLMAN, T.W.C.	Vol.91, pp.33-36,	*Thecla betulae*
	pp.154-156 (1979)	
WILLMOTT, K.J.	Vol.103, pp.247-249 (1991)	*Hesperia comma*

WILDLIFE LAWS

Readers should ensure that they are aware of the current legislation in any country in which they intend take specimens or use a net. Laws vary from country to country and even between regions within a country, the most restrictive prohibiting even the carrying of collecting equipment.

In Great Britain some insects have been given full protection under the Wildlife and Countryside Act of 1981, with its subsequent additions and amendments. Currently (year 2001) it is illegal to take any stage of the following butterfly species from the wild: Heath Fritillary, High Brown Fritillary, Marsh Fritillary, Swallowtail, Large Blue, Large Copper. The habitat where these species exist is also protected and it is an offence to damage, destroy or prevent access to such places or to disturb or kill any protected species. Possession of or trading in specimens (whether dead or alive) of any of the above species is also an offence unless it can be proven that they or their progenitors were collected from the wild before the species concerned became fully protected. If, however, such proof can be shown, it is possible under section 16 of the Act to obtain a licence to trade.

It is also illegal to trade in any stage of the following species without a licence: Adonis Blue, Black Hairstreak, Brown Hairstreak, Chalkhill Blue, Chequered Skipper, Duke of Burgundy Fritillary, Glanville Fritillary, Large Heath, Large Tortoiseshell, Lulworth Skipper, Mountain Ringlet, Northern Brown Argus, Pearl-bordered Fritillary, Purple Emperor, Silver Spotted Skipper, Silver Studded Blue, Small Blue, White Letter Hairstreak, Wood White. In essence the aim of this part of the Act is to ensure that traders only sell stock which has been continuously bred in captivity, i.e. not bred directly from a wild female or any other stage collected in the wild. There are also various degrees of legal protection provided within the Acts for some moths and other invertebrates.

If you are purchasing stock from anyone, please ensure you are buying from a reputable source and check that they have obtained the necessary licence to trade. The origin of any protected species should be clearly stated by dealers and dead specimens labelled accordingly. If they are from captive bred stock this should be clearly stated on the label, otherwise it may be presumed to have been taken from the wild.

Currently the Wildlife (Northern Ireland) Order 1985 affords full protection in Northern Ireland to the following butterflies which must not be offered for sale or collected from the wild in any stage: Brimstone, Dingy Skipper, Holly Blue, Large Heath, Marsh Fritillary, Purple Hairstreak, Small Blue.

The above is only a short summary of the main features of the Acts at the time of publication and can only act as a guide to the law. The onus is on individual dealers, purchasers of stock and those taking specimens from the wild to ensure that they are acting fully within the Wildlife and Countryside Acts that are current at that time. Further details including the conditions and issuing of licences can be obtained from:

Department of the Environment, Transport and the Regions
Global Wildlife Division
Tollgate House
Houlton Street
Bristol BS2 9DJ

Alternatively visit their web site at: http://www.wildlife-countryside.detr.gov.uk